MW00653200

The Pool and the Portal!

Robin D. Bullock

The Pool and the Portal!

YFMCI Publishing www.robindbullock.com
P.O. Box 67 Warrior, Al 35180-0067 USA

Orders: www.robindbullock.com

Copyright 2018

All rights reserved. No part of this book may be reproduced or transmitted in any form or by any means, electronic, or mechanical, including photocopying, recording, or by any information storage and retrieval system, without written permission from the author, except for the inclusion of brief quotations for a review.

All scripture quotations are taken from the King James Version of the Bible unless otherwise noted.

ISBN: 978-0-9722539-0-1

Credits:
Edits by: Roxanne Sanderson and John Bullock
Cover Art: Madison Eden
Back Cover Layout: John Bullock

Printed in the USA
by Walk With Me Ministries, Inc.

PREFACE

A Note from the author:
This book is a novel that began with a dream I had, concerning a hideous green pool. It is a novel that contains both fact and fiction.

Just suppose there are plans being made that are far more sinister than the average person has ever imagined! And just suppose that there are men and women in high positions of government that know it and make their plans accordingly!

What if I told you that just such a plan was devised years ago and put into motion in 2008?

What could Seven men, Satan, Ahab, Jezebel, Jehu, and modern day politicians all have to do with one another? The parallels between the modern day and ancient public figures named in this book are amazing. Whether or not modern day people are fulfilling these parallels on purpose or unknowing to them we do not know.

Some would call this book fiction; some would say nonsense while some will ponder it with great thought. Then there are some who will read the writings within this book with entirely different thoughts: like "how did he know?" Any way you read it, once you have, you will never think on certain things the same way again!

Table
Of
Contents

Chapter 1

Hell Beneath Is Stirred Up

A Hideous winged creature with eyes of cold death, stood at the edge of a large pool filled with green liquid. The pool was filled with crocodile looking creatures. It was wretched looking; there was steam rising up from it and the tips of large rocks showing just above the surface. The dark creature stood and watched as one by one the faces of people rolled up to the surface of the green liquid. Each one's head clenched tightly sideways in the mouth of one of the reptile creatures! Their faces frozen horrified with their teeth grit and their eyes open in fear!

Total disgust showed on the winged creature's face, as he watched familiar faces like Adolf Hitler roll to the surface only to be submerged once again! Just then a slosh was heard in the left of the pool. The creature turned to look as one of the reptiles rolled up to the surface, regaining its bite on a human head.

Nimrod, he thought, *what a fool!*

"Nimrod!" the creature called out.

When he did, the crocodile held his head where he had to look at the winged being in the face and listen to him, adding to his torment!

"You sold out Nimrod! You sold yourself and the humans

around you! You offered gallons of human blood on the altar to Satan, trying to mingle your seed with ours. You did everything you could to give Satan the earth! You stupid fool! You tried to become half angel. Look at you now, just a deformed fool. Millions are still coming here because of you!" He chuckled out loud as he mocked him.

"This is the reward you get for it! You thought you would be one of the new creatures? Surprise you idiot!" he said laughing out, as he walked off. "Because of you we still have them killing their own children! Nimrod, THE FATHER OF ABORTION!"

The crocodile then rolled Nimrod's petrified face back under the green pool. The winged creature continued laughing!

"Soon the earth will be empty of all of you; YOU, YOU, MEN!" he said searching for the vilest words he could to attach to them.

It won't be long now, he thought. *More and more humans keep coming to this place daily, by their own choice! Satan is killing all of those that he can, who won't follow him. We must be winning, he thought. Why else would so many of God's images be coming here every day? The knowledge has come down through caverns of the damned, that the door is about to open, and we will finally pour into the earth and it will be ours!*

"HA! HA! HA!" his laughter echoed through hell. "Then we will finally get to feast on these creatures daily!"

The winged creatures name was Sä·na'. He was in charge of the region of hell that is stirred up to greet humans as they arrive! The cesspool of green liquid was merely a temporary holding cell, until a future time.

Sä·na' hated humans, he hated everything about them and he enjoyed watching them suffer! He liked seeing their faces as they froze in fear the first time they saw the pool, and the thought of what was about to happen to them!

Sä·na' liked hearing the sound of the crocodile like creatures biting down on their heads; in fact, it made him chuckle! Just then, Sä·na''s thoughts were interrupted when a young woman about 20 years old surfaced in the pool. Sä·na' almost growled out loud in hate as he took his foot and shoved her head back under!

It's just a matter of time, Sä·na' thought as he looked up, *that lid will open, and then,* "HA! WE RULE! HA! HA! HA!" The creature laughed so loud that it echoed through the caverns of hell! It started a chain reaction of laughter through the halls of the damned!

****

Intelligence data:

> Humans have very little perception of these beings. These creatures have no blood; therefore they have no respect for blood! These creatures have no compassion and no mercy at all!

> You can see a small manifestation of these beings in the natural when you see a possessed man go into a school or church with a gun and kill people including small children while all the while the child stares up at them in horror! Or a doctor who can rip a baby limb from limb in the womb, while the little child is kicking and fighting to get away from the surgical instruments. Then when they have torn them apart sell the body parts that are intact to the highest bidder!

> The creatures in the kingdom of darkness hate each

other. They are all fighting for position; the creatures below do not know everything going on here. They only perceive by the evil people falling into the damned every day. They are confused and they are afraid, and they are evil to their very core! People who are cast into hell lose their souls (their minds, wills and emotions) therefore they have no resistance at all. The demonic spirits and evil that exist there are tortured also and are looking for relief. A spirit of fear, for instance, is just that: afraid! They are the very depths of fear and so is every spirit of whatever evil it is. Once someone is there, whatever hideous being is there can move in and out of their souls at will! They are searching for relief so they move in and out of the human soul hoping for a moment of relief.

> There are different levels of hell; this pool is just one of them. Satan's grand plan has always been to be flesh and blood. He would trade it all to be a man, (in the image of God or like he said: to be like the Most High!).

* *

Suddenly, there was a loud chilling sound of huge bodies slamming themselves against the walls! It shook the whole place! Sä·na' whirled around in fear! It reminded him of an event a couple thousand years back! Then he chuckled, when he realized what it was; *ah the chained ones,* he thought. *Satan was smart to have used them to co-habitat with human women instead of his own self; he knew if the plan failed, those fools would reap the harvest instead of him!*

Of course, Sä·na' thought, *that's the way Satan is, he will always leave someone else to pay for what he does. These fools never think of this, but I do. Satan only leads these beings around like fools because he understands more about the law than any of them.*

Just then he heard them lunge again, "Oh chained ones, when I'm in control, there may still be a way to free you!"

Sä·na''s gaze kept looking upward to a large grey metal-looking lid, his gaze was always looking that way, lately more and more, as if he was expecting something to happen soon.

Sä·na' pushed open a large wooden-looking door with giant metal hinges. When it opened the most vial odor filled the atmosphere! Its smell would have removed the air in any room and made the strongest man fall to the ground! It was unlike any smell on earth! It wreaked of vomited up death!

When Sä·na' entered the room, the odor hung visible like a green cloud in the atmosphere. He took a deep breath into his demonic lungs breathing the green odor inside himself. Sä·na' smiled a hideous smile like someone who enjoyed eating human bones.

As he looked around the room at the creatures in it he thought to himself; *The great hoard! The earth and the remnant of those crimson filled beings will not know what hit them, when this army is released into the earth!*

The room was filled with the sounds of hissing, licking and nasally squeals! Then suddenly with the voice of a thousand tortured dying men, Sä·na' screamed out, "SHUT UP!"

All the room went silent with fear! Sä·na' was the chief lieutenant in charge of the bottomless pit. He was preparing a fallen army to invade the earth! As he stood there he started to remember all that had passed leading up to this moment.

"We must prepare," he said. "Soon the portal will open!"

As Sä·na' remembered, his pride rose up in him and he shouted out: "I was there! I was great! I was marvelous! There was no one like me! Then, I spoke from inside the great pyramid sanctuary, where I controlled the gravitational pulls for this whole sector of creation! There were 1/3 of us chosen to do these things, but I was THE GREATEST! HA, HA, HA, HA, HA" Sä·na' laughed in pride!

Suddenly the creatures in the room broke out into shrills and squeals. When they did the green visible odor grew thicker in the room, as the creatures belched it out of their lungs!

"It's been a long time since many of you have seen Satan," Sä·na' said, "but he will return for us one day, and bring us to where he is!"

"Yes," Sä·na' said out loud, "then we'll be caught up together through that great portal to the earth!"

"THE EARTH! THE EARTH!" Sä·na' shouted, "THE PROMISED LAND!"

Chapter 2

The Grand Plan

The year is 2008, in an undisclosed location, just out of sight and sound of human ears; Satan stood staring at seven men. The seven pawns he uses to run his earthly Babylonian system. The seven men seated in the room, could not see Satan and his chief lieutenant watching them, but they had become very used to the presence of the dark kingdom around them.

While principalities and powers, and rulers of the darkness of this world and spiritual wickedness in high places were about their business, Satan his self was spending all his time with these seven who had freely given themselves to him!

These men and their families run the world financially; this is an ancient group. Every war is fought according to them, recessions, depressions; everything is manipulated by their decisions. Over time as one or two of the seven representatives die off, those that have been groomed to take their place have to receive a detailed briefing about the Grand Plan! This was a day they had met to do just that.

As the seven men sat waiting, one man with greying hair and hollow eyes motioned to a guard. The guard opened a door and a confident young woman in her mid-20's walked into the room. She was trained all of her life for one purpose: to brief the panel of new comers. The greying man gestured to her, and with a cold, calculating, voice that sounded as if it could slaughter a million children with no remorse, said to her, "Tell in detail, The Grand Plan!"

The woman briefing the panel had spent her life studying the plan along with several others. She was convinced that the day would come that she would be rewarded with great power, wealth and riches! Little did she know that after she finished this briefing she would be murdered! She would never be allowed to know what she knows and risk telling it. She was bred ritually and born in secret. There was no record of her birth or her ever existing. She had been educated her whole life and her whole reason for being was to brief new comers. Of course it was told to her and the others that would replace her, that she would be carried away to retire in luxury in an undisclosed place, with a new identity! The young woman had no idea the fear that awaited her as she would be hideously offered in sacrifice to the goddess Shiva in front of the great particle collider!

"Give us a complete update on the Grand Plan and leave nothing out," the man said.

"Yes sir," the young woman answered.

As she opened a large ancient-looking binder, Satan watched her and said to his chief lieutenant, "Go, fill her yielded mouth with words."

The nasty spirit moved quickly to the young woman. It looked as if he grafted himself to her! As the demonic creature over whelmed the woman with his presence, suddenly a crooked smile came over her face, and she began.

"Since our inception and our first contact with the fallen ones, to this present time April 28, 2008, we've made considerable progress. Thanks to Adam after he fell, prompted by fear, he began his search trying to return back to his position. He showed us how to open the door and contact the fallen ones on the other side of the light line. Once we learned how to open the door to the dimension of fallen angels, we were able to bring them over! Oh, and this sir, is when we began to first learn how to create flesh covered crimson; the hybrid seed." When she said this, she almost broke out in laughter.

"Sirs," she continued, "the science was all right. But if the portal to that dimension opened with the wrong force behind it, disaster would follow! It seems that somehow, in some way, before Adam fell he could open the portals and never cause a strain here. It was seamless how he did this. The hybrids multiplied in the earth until there were only eight purebred's left! The man Noah and his family somehow gained information that a worldwide flood was coming! He prepared a great vessel, a ship. He and his family, and a select number of animals loaded on that vessel and were saved from the flood, to begin again on the earth."

"However sirs," she continued, "we, for some reason, never saw it coming and as a result, not one of the great ones escaped! Even though their stature was great, giants in the earth, they still did not escape! Their bodies can still be seen encased in stone upon the high mountains in Idaho, and in different places around the world."

She continued "Unfortunately, the knowledge Adam possessed of how to open dimensions was lost to all but the eight and they forbade it from being told. Adam knew it was coming, but by this time he had turned from us and was following with the few pure breeds that were left. However, Adam did leave a history of what happened on two pillars he erected in the valley of Shinar, so that after the flood the knowledge of what happened and why would not be lost. This would later prove to be of great help to us. The eight that were saved from the deluge knew how to unlock the hidden knowledge in the pillars but they would not speak of it. They guarded THEIR IMAGINATIONS. But as you know sirs, the great force of greed and lust always prevails!" The seven men smiled as they looked at each other. For each one had abused a child the night before!

"These forces born into the purebreds helped us. The master himself was able to use these powerful forces and along with their natural curiosity, we found our ally through Noah's son, Ham. The dark imaginations began to stir again, and through Ham came the great Nimrod!" At the mention of Nimrod, all the men grew suddenly reverent.

****

Intelligence Data:

> Nimrod was like a god among these powerful men. Their whole organization was based on Nimrods beliefs and philosophy. Nimrod tapped into the dark arts so powerfully that he himself began to transform into a hybrid! A giant, a gibboreem!

> Nimrod began to offer blood on the altar of Baal, the key ingredient to bring the fallen ones into this atmosphere. Nimrod and the fallen beings figured the plan was safe because God had already promised another flood would not come. And even if a flood came the Tower would be high enough to protect them.

****

"His tower dedicated to the dark arts was almost complete," the woman continued with her briefing. "However the people began to get different ideas, different beliefs and became con-fused. This slowed down our spread of the knowledge in their imaginations. By cross breeding and the mingling of multiple men and animal seeds along with the dark rituals, we were able to have a form of giants once again. However, they were not as large as those in the days of old. With the confusion and scattering of the people, and after Shem killed Nimrod, the giant program looked in jeopardy. Some of Hams descendants scattered and settled in Egypt. There they employed Adams original knowledge of how to bring the fallen ones over to this side."

"Now sir, we come to the Osiris device, the Ta-Wer, or as we call it, the Star Gate Machine! It was capable of opening wormholes into other dimensions! If Adam had not encoded the knowledge of this on the pillar he erected in Shinar after the great flood, we may never have found it again!"

****

Intelligence Data:

> Adam's seat used to be in heaven. The tabernacle that Moses built at the instruction of the LORD was after the pattern of the tabernacle in heaven. Moses was told to be sure and build it exactly after the pattern of the one in heaven.

> In the tabernacle in heaven, there was an outer court, where the Brazen Altar was. There was a Laver for the water, there was an inner court where the Menorah, the seven branched golden candle stick stood, there is the original Table of Shewbread and the Golden Altar of incense, then there is the Holy of Holies. The Holiest place of all!

> This tabernacle was the sanctuary for God and man to fellowship. It contained all mysteries shared between the two. Here God could call Adam into the inner court, the

classroom where the revelation of God is learned.

> Then Adam would go and sit down on the heavenly Ark of the Covenant (Of Sonship) which sat at the right hand of God. They were so one with each other that they would sit together in that throne as Father and son and reign together. This is why there had to be a substituted Blood placed on the mercy seat in the Tabernacle of Moses. It represented the mercy seat in heaven where Adam, the blood man, used to sit! The enormity of the power of the covenant it represented could bend light and open a portal for Adam, a flesh and blood man, to go to heaven and come back again! After the fall Adam tried to duplicate the heavenly ark with the Ta-Wer, in an attempt to open a portal back to heaven and regain his position.

* *

As the woman continued her briefing, there was uneasy silence; "The Ta-Wer," she said, "produced an enormous amount of energy! So much so that it was actually able to bend two points of light and produce a space time tunnel that matter could actually pass through! When the light was bent and the portals opened on either end, two of the fallen ones, Seth and Osiris, began to travel back and forth from the underworld."

The man in charge studied the faces of the new ones to see how they were processing all of this. The woman reading turned the page.

"With these two fallen ones traveling back and forth," she continued "we were able to learn more of the lost knowledge again."

Just then the lights went down in the room and a 3D hologram appeared in the center of the room.

"The TA-Wer, the Osiris device!" she said excitedly.

The image was so real it seemed you could touch it!

"Our brethren actually drew this image on the sacred walls of the pyramids. This, gentlemen, is known as the Boat of a Million Years! They not only drew it, but they also wrote down the knowledge of how it worked in the mysterious hieroglyphs! This is what has allowed us to build the giant collider in Switzerland."

Just then, the image of the TA-Wer went away and the image of the giant Hadron particle collider appeared in its place!

"In 1949 we put this on the board for production." she explained. "Our first attempt at bringing entities into our dimension was disastrous. However, it has gotten extremely more accurate and efficient over time. The last time we powered it up, it bent light on two ends so powerful that it rattled the enormous lid on the other side! Through the knowledge we have gained over the centuries from Seth and Osiris, we now have a precise time for this."

As the lights came up the young woman turned the page.

Chapter 3

The Prophecy

"Now sirs," she said, "I will go over the prophecy. Through the dark order of the Masonic, working through the Presidency of The United States, we were able to print the prophecy of the Cumaean Sybil on the back of the United States currency itself!"

Just then, the leader of the seven interrupted and looking over at the new members said, "We have successfully been able to seize most of the power in the most powerful nation in the earth, The United States! Through our Masonic order when every American President is inaugurated, at the moment they are being sworn in, our brethren raise the spirit of Osiris to come and embody every American President."

"Does it work?" one of the new ones ask.

"Most of the time it works," he answered, "however sometimes it does not." He explained, "A lot of the Presidents were Masons throughout history, yet they never fully realized the connotations of the darkness they were involved in. This ignorance allowed us to infiltrate enough of congress and judges around the nation with enough of our brethren to get done what we needed to, which is to advance the agenda. While the U.S. Congress is powerful to us, none is as important as the judges around the United States. We have been able to convince the people through them that the judges make the laws instead of just interpreting them."

"You see," he continued, "through the Masonic order, the great prophecy of the Cumaean Sibyl "NOVUS ORDO SECLORUM" is on every one dollar bill in America! With it on the one dollar bill, the great prophecy is handled and spread by even the most common person!"

"Ah, the prophecy," he said as he sat back in his chair. The evil leader seemed to, for just a moment, have the features of a serpent as he closed his eyes and smiled!

He then began to quote parts of the prophecy of the Cumaen Sibyl:

"Now the last age by Cumae's Sibyl sung has come and gone, and the majestic roll of circling centuries begins anew: justice returns, returns old Saturn's reign, with a new breed of men sent down from heaven. Only do thou, at the boys birth in whom the iron shall cease, the golden race arise, befriend him chaste Lucina; tis thine own Apollo reigns."

As he finished quoting parts of the ancient prophecy the rest of the panel began to applaud!

With great pride the leader smiled!

"Everything is in place," he said. "Apollo will return and the country who is the financial leader of the world is paying for it," he said, as they all began to laugh.

* *

Intelligence Data:

> The Cumaean Sybil was the most important prophetess of Apollo. In one painting she appears to be a six fingered giant, who resembles part man and part woman. This

sybil is prominently featured in the Sistine Chapel at the Vatican, and is given a place of honor among the prophets of the Bible. This Sybil was the most important among the Pythians. They operated in the spirit of divination, the python or serpent spirit. This goes all the way back to the Garden of Eden when the serpent first spoke to the woman.

> There are two things written on the back of the One dollar bill, Annuit Coeptis & Novus Ordo Seclorum.

> Annuit Coeptis is taken from Vergil's Aeneid IX:625. It means, He (Jupiter) favors our undertaking. Jupiter is the father of Apollo!

> "NOVUS ORDO SECLORUM, "New Order of The Ages" this was taken from a prophecy of the Cumaean Sybil recorded in Vergil's Eclogues IV: 5.

> It predicts that at the end of time there will come the arrival of the divine son, Apollo.

****

Just then Satan's chief demon lieutenant left the young woman and returned to Satan's side. "Master," he said, "once we have a piece of eternity in our hands, and we are finally able to operate in the future, what then?"

Satan turned and looked at him with eyes of total hopelessness and growled his answer in a mysterious statement, "It is time to resurrect my throne!"

"Your throne," the creature responded, "but how? It hasn't been in power since your servant Hitler!"

"I'm going to raise it, but this time in the most powerful nation on the earth!" Satan answered.

"The United States of America," the demonic lieutenant whispered.

"Yes!" The dark murderer scowled as he turned his gaze back toward the seven men. "Through the party of their government that has offered me the blood of millions of children! There has been enough blood sacrifice's to me through abortion, that it has now changed their mentalities totally! I now have murderers in high offices; I also have them in the lowest levels of the people! They don't even think about abortion being murder anymore, they only think about money! They are now operating in my anointing! Their mindset has changed so, that now they are selling the body parts of their own young! Now is the time, I will raise it again!"

* *

Intelligence Data: The Throne of Satan

> 1. In the time of ancient Israel, the image of the false god, Baal, was placed on the high places of Israel. Children were offered to it as human sacrifice.
>
> 2. In the time of the Maccabees, the greek king Antiochus set up an idol to Zeus in the temple of The LORD!
>
> 3. Antiochus defiled the temple.
>
> 4. The Maccabees took back the temple and cleansed it (This is the whole Chanukah story).
>
> 5. After the Maccabees tore down the altar of Zeus and took back the temple, eventually it reappeared in the place

called Pergamon. In the book of The Revelation, it is called the Throne of Satan.

6. In the late 19th century, a man started excavation of The Pergamon altar or The Throne of Satan. He sent the peices of the altar back to his homeland of Germany. Eventually, the Throne of Satan was assemble in Berlin. The year it was finished, Adolf Hitler was born in Austria!

7. As they were building a massive place to house "The Throne of Satan", WW2 broke out!

8. When Hitler became the dictator of Germany, the platform he spoke from in Nuremberg was patterned after The Throne of Satan.

9. The WW2 generation is known as the greatest generation that ever lived! They fought the greatest evil we have ever known in modern time.

10. In this generation, Satan had resurrected his throne and was going to take over the world! He was going to annihilate the Jewish people. WW2 was a war against God and all that is holy. The WW2 Generation was raised up to defeat this! At the same time there were evangelists raised up to defeat the devil in the spirit and to pray. Together they defeated The Throne of Satan!

Chapter 4

Micah Cross

Seven years had passed. It was now 2015. The plan of the dark world had progressed until it was time to execute it! The target date was September!

Micah Cross was a warrior and a strategist in the Kingdom of God. Micah lived his life by the Word of God and through the Word of God and the Spirit of God. Micah had access to all the intel and he actually believed the intel. This made him very usable by the Kingdom of Heaven, but at the same time this made him very dangerous to the Kingdom of Hell!

Micah believed that making Jesus Christ the Lord of your life is the only way to heaven. He knew philosophies like co-exist and the melting of all religions as equal were filling up hell every day! Micah believed that the Holy Bible is actually God in written form, and that to live and be an effective warrior one had to make the Word of God final authority in their life!

Even though there were millions of other Christians who believed these things also, Micah believed something that not many others did, he believed that God Is Absolutely Good! That God never allows bad to come on anyone in a causative sense! Or that God would test or try anyone to see what they would do! Believing this gave him the edge in spiritual combat!

He believed in the Baptism of the Mighty Holy Ghost, with His nine gifts! Micah believed that the ability to pray and speak in other tongues, as the Spirit gave him utterance was the original language God and Adam spoke to one another in before Adam fell. He also believed that this language gave him the ability to speak the mysteries of God, and that it gave him access to the keys of the Kingdom of Heaven, which is revelation knowledge.

Micah Cross knew that not many Christians believed all these things, oh, but he did! He believed that God wrote His voice down so that one could not misunderstand it!

The warrior was feared by the Kingdom of Hell, because he was a true warrior in the spirit. He walked in the office of apostle, prophet and teacher. Micah Cross didn't fit in anywhere and yet at the same time he fit in everywhere! With his brown shoulder length hair and groomed beard, Micah, a prophetic musician, carried an anointing similar to King David. He had served God 30 of the 40 years he had been on the earth! Micah did everything he knew to keep his life in a position to hear the voice of God, and constantly be led by the Holy Spirit.

Micah Cross was well aware of the worlds beyond what you could see with your natural eyes or hear with your natural ears. He knew that the beings of those worlds were organized and were at constant war for the souls of men. The Kingdom of Heaven was after the souls of men for love of the race, while the Kingdom of Darkness wanted control of the earth! While Micah knew of both worlds, it was a two way street, the spirit world also knew Micah Cross.

There was a plan that had gone unseen by most of the Christian world, and was just about to come into being! Through a series of revelations, the Holy Spirit had been showing Micah a strategy the kingdom of darkness had planned, that if allowed to come to pass, it would be devastating!
****

Intelligence Data:

> In the world before Adam was created, Satan's name was Lucifer. It was a God given name that means "Light Bearer!"

> Jesus - The Word Himself - also has a title as the leader of the angelic host known as, El-Gibbor - God the Mighty Warrior!

> Jesus being the second member of the eternal God head, created the angelic armies, He is also called "The Bright and The Morning Star!"

> Lucifer was known as the son of the morning, Lucifer was Jesus' personal angel.

> Lucifer was anointed to walk up and down in the midst of the stones of fire and find revelation in those stones and carry it to the earth.

> Lucifer was the high priest of the world before Adam was created.

> As the high priest he wore an ephod of every precious stone. The sardius, topaz, and the diamond, the beryl, the onyx, and the jasper, the sapphire, the emerald, and the carbuncle, and gold:

> With ten items on his ephod (10 the number of Law) he operated in the law of God and totally understood it.

> He had tambourines built into him instead of a heart.

> He had pipes-like instruments prepared in him in the day he was created, by Jesus the Word of God himself!

> The beings in the earth in those days were not men. They were in the animal class. They were monkey-like beings with high intelligence. They, as well as the whole earth, were in total submission to the angelic world.

> It was a legal rule of angels, a military rule, yet an army of holiness and purity.

> The anointed cherub was set on a throne on the holy mountain of God, this mountain is known as Jericho. Jericho also means the Moon!

> In those days the earth was surrounded with a canopy of thin metalic plates, known as crystalline. It kept the earth a perfect environment. It only let in the proper amount of ultra violet rays, and in those days, ferns would grow 120 feet in the air.

> There is an altar of God filled with stones of fire.

> When the trinity God created everything, He wrote a series of letters first. There are 22 letters in this series. Each letter was given a title: Aleph, Bet, Gimel, Dalet, Heh, Vav, Zayin, Chet, Tet, Yod, Kaf, Lamed, Mem, Nun, Samech, Ayin, Pe, Tsadhe, Quoph, Resh, Shin, and Tav. These were burned into His majestic crown! He took these and wrote with black fire on white fire, and wrote The Holy Book. The Torah!

> This Holy Book was also given a name "Sophia" or "Wisdom" He then consulted with Wisdom and created.

> The Great Revelations of His Word are burning stones of fire.

> Lucifer was anointed with his name, "Light Bearer" To

walk up and down in the midst of these stones and find a revelation.

> These stones contained the revelations from the "Mind of God." The Light Bearer had a very unique anointing of a musician.

> With his tabrets and pipes, he became a living instrument!

> He would walk up and down in the midst of the stones of Revelation and when he would find a revelation, he would spread his wings with a span of around 20 feet and lift himself up to the center of the earth. When he did, those tabrets would begin to beat with the rhythm of the life pulsating through the earth and he would sing the Revelations in a prophetic tone. The sound would hit the crystalline canopy and that canopy would carry the sound all the way around the earth, and fruitful places would grow and cities would be built by the creatures in this planet.

> While walking up and down in the midst of the stones of fire Lucifer saw a revelation that made him realize the creation wasn't for him, it was for a being called MAN!

> The angel did not know what a man was exactly, but he found him there in The Stones of Fire! In The Mind of God! Who was he! Whoever he was, he was going to have children and God Himself was going to visit him!

> He took this to the high court of heaven, and earnestly protested!

> As the high court of heaven convened, the position character and authority of God known as YHVH "God in His

government of Law," this is the part of Elohim that angels go before. As the court came to order Lucifer began his protest as the whole court set in silence in disbelief that any creature, especially this one, would dare challenge God! The very creator of all life! Absolute Goodness Himself! And yet Lucifer continued:

> "O YHVH our Master how excellent is your authority in all the earth! Who hast set your glory above the heavens. Out of the mouth of babes and suckling's have you ordained strength because of your enemies, that thou mightest still the enemy and the avenger. When I consider your heavens, the work of your fingers, the moon and the stars, which you have ordained; what is man, that you are mindful of him and the son of man, that you would visit him? For you have made him a little lower than Elohim, and has crowned him with glory and honor. You made him to have dominion over the works of your hands; thou hast put all things under his feet: All sheep and oxen, yea, and the beasts of the field; the fowl of the air, and the fish of the sea, and whatsoever passeth through the paths of the seas. O YHVH our Master, how excellent is your authority in all the earth! (Psalm chapter 8 and Hebrews chapter 2)

> This was his protest and the beginning of his down fall.

> He did not know there was a position open between him and God! The thought of being subordinate to another being was more than he could stand. It filled him with violence!

> Lucifer plotted a coup! A Hostile military overthrow! His motive: HE WANTED THE POSITION OF THE MAN!

> Lucifer had found out more about the man that was coming. That this man would sit with God in the mount of

the congregation where God's throne sat in the North! He knew that man was in the image and the likeness of God!

> Lucifer was given sanctuaries, the great pyramids; this is where he gave instruction to the inhabitants of the earth, as to their part in preparing the earth with fruitful places and cities.

> Lucifer from his sanctuaries began to traffic or merchandises his anointing. He began to trade it for worship and allegiance. He began to lie and slander God! He convinced 1/3 of the angelic armies to follow him.

> Lucifer thought his anointing would make his own words come to pass also, not knowing that his anointing as a prophetic musician was only to carry Gods Words of Revelation to the earth!

> Lucifer declared:

- "I will ascend into heaven,"

- I will exalt my throne above the stars of God: (By throne he was saying "I will also create flesh covered crimson.")

- "I will sit also upon the mount of the congregation in the sides of the north:"

- "I will ascend above the heights of the clouds;"

- "I will be like the most high."

Isaiah 14:13-14

Chapter 5

Patterns and Cycles

The battle had heated up more than most anyone had realized. Micah was being maneuvered into a very strategic position by the Spirit of God. In 1992 Micah Cross began to study something very unique: patterns and cycles!

It looked like a war room in Micah's study. From all the charts on the walls, to the manila envelopes on his desk; each one filled with information that you would rarely hear said anywhere.

"Ah here it is," Micah said, as he pulled the file labeled Ahab & Jezebel.

Opening it he began to read:

- In ancient Israel there was a king named Ahab who had a wife named Jezebel. Ahab wore the crown, but his wife had the power! During their reign babies were slaughtered like never before (Offered to a false god called Baal).

- During their reign, there was a land scandal over a vineyard owned by a man named Naboth. The King stood to gain by acquiring this piece of land, but Naboth wouldn't sell. Therefore Jezebel deceived the people, had Naboth killed, and seized the land.

- Ahab did more to provoke God to anger than any other

king before him.

- This king was wounded in battle during his time as king, but he managed to stay up in his chariot until the end of the day, then he died.

- His people washed all the blood out of his chariot.

- His wife, Jezebel decided she wanted to run the nation. So she went back to the palace and started setting up her kingdom.

- At this time The Prophet Elisha sent a prophet to anoint a certain war Captain named Jehu to be the next king over Israel.

- This particular Captain was the grandson of a man named "Nimshi," which means, "extricated" or, "freed from a constraint or difficulty". This famous war captain started campaigning furiously across the land.

Micah looked up as he began to soak these things in. He knew that this was a cycle that had been turning since the early 1990's. However, the trail seemed to disappear and the pattern had become more obscure in recent times. But now the Spirit of God had him looking at it again. Micah knew something about the enemy that only a few did. The enemy was bound to operate in these cycles; Satan couldn't do anything outside of the system of seed time and harvest. Micah continued to read:

- Captain Jehu confronted Jezebel at the palace.

- Jezebel painted her face, walked out, and looked down out of a window at the captain, and began to debate him!

- Jehu looked up and called out "Who is with me?"

- Two or three Eunuchs stepped up and looked down at him.

- Jehu said, THROW HER DOWN!

- Her own people threw her down.

- Some of her blood splattered against the wall!

- The war Captain and his chariots ran over her body!

- When it was all over, all you could find of her was part of her skull, her feet and the palms of her hands!

- At the palace, the dogs ate her flesh.

- Captain Jehu buried what was left of her.

- Israel then had a new leader!

Micah knew he was matching wits with a creature that had been around for thousands of years. He knew this creature had manipulated humans and situations using the knowledge of these cycles. Micah stopped, looked up, and thanked God for the mind of Christ and the Holy Spirit for guiding him in this war!

He began to go over the facts about this cycle. First, he had to apply the rule of this cycle. *Israel,* Micah thought, *the covenant Nation, the natural olive tree in which the body of Christ is grafted into, the chosen people through which Messiah came.*

"Nothing happens to mankind that does not have a connection to Israel somewhere or somehow," Micah said under his breath. "The USA is directly connected to Israel."

Micah knew the United States of America was almost named Israel. He also knew that Christopher Columbus was hunting a new home for the Jewish people, when he landed here. Israel was created because God loved Israel. America was created because America loved God. Because of this, every major political event in America can be found in scripture.

Micah began to go over the intel of Ahab and Jezebel again.

Micah knew that every detail meant something. So meticulously, he continued.

This puzzle has large pieces, Micah thought. *If I match the parallels of these events, I can see not only what has happened, but what is happening now and more important, WHAT WILL HAPPEN!*

"Praise God," Micah said out loud. "Wait a minute," he blurted out. "Of course," he began to write faster now.

"The answer is staring us right in the face! It's been hidden in plain view," Micah said.

He began to draw the parallel.

> *Ahab became king over Israel. Ahab had the title as King, but his wife, Jezebel, had the power.
> *Bill Clinton became The President of the United States. Bill Clinton had the title as President, but his wife had the power.
>
> *During Ahab and Jezebel's reign, babies were offered to Baal.
> *During Bill and Hillary Clinton's terms the killing of Babies in abortions grew huge.

*Jezebel had Naboth killed for his land (his vineyard).
*During Bill and Hillary Clinton's terms, there was a huge land scandal and someone was found murdered.
*After this, the Clintons vacationed in Martha's Vineyard.

*During Ahab's time as king, he was mortally wounded in battle but managed to hold himself up until the end of the day.
*During Bill Clinton's time as President, he was politically wounded (impeached) but he never left office. He managed to hold himself in office until the end of his terms.

*The people washed Ahab's chariot clean.
*When Bill Clinton left office, his people made him a hero as if nothing had happened.

*After Ahab's death, Jezebel stayed in the palace.
*After Bill Clinton left office, eventually his wife (Hillary Clinton) decided to stay in government.

*After Ahab had died, Jezebel ran the nation, but God gave His people someone to anoint after Ahab, a famous war captain named Jehu.
*When Bill Clinton left office, eventually Hillary decided like Jezebel, that she wanted to be the President and run the nation, and like in Jehu's time, God gave His people someone to vote for! A famous war captain named John McCain!

*God's people would not support John McCain. (It dawned on Micah, Elijah didn't anoint Jehu either! And neither did Elisha! Elisha sent another prophet to do it).

*Jehu was the son of Nimshi which means (Extricated) or freed from a constraint!
*John McCain was a famous war Captain, famous for being

freed from being a prisoner of war, or extricated! It all fit the pattern!

Micah Cross did not believe in coincidences, but even if he did, this is too spot-on to be a coincidence. Then the thought hit Micah: *this happened at a place called Jezreel!*

Micah knew that every word in the Bible was significant. He scrambled for his Hebrew concordance to see what the name Jezreel meant.

There it was, *Jezreel, God sows!* Of course, Micah thought. *This that happened at Jezreel, was a seed planted here for future events!*

Micah had spent years studying the government of God, which is seed, plant and harvest! Therefore, he knew that nothing happens without a seed being planted for it. The story of Ahab and Jezebel was all seed, and it was coming up in the extended soil of Israel, the United States of America!

In 2008 Jezebel's (Hillary Clinton's) own people sure enough threw her off the wall, and put up Barak Obama in her place! Micah began to think on Barak Obama! He scrambled for his computer as he began to research. Jezebel was thrown down, Barak Obama was put up in her place, Henry Kissinger made the statement that Barak Obama was groomed to bring in THE NEW WORLD ORDER!

This is a plan! Micah thought to himself. *This is all a plan and certain men know it!* Barak Obama seemed to mesmerize people when he spoke! He had every characteristic of the anti-Christ, yet Micah knew he wasn't the anti-Christ, but he was a type of the anti-Christ.

Micah stared at the intel as he read Luke 10:18: "***And he said***

unto them, I beheld Satan as lightning fall from heaven."

This scripture actually read in Hebrew, "I beheld Satan as Barak O Bamah!"

Things began to shape up quickly in Micah's mind. He walked around his prophetic war room and began to put puzzle pieces together!

In 2013 the miniseries "The Bible" came out. In the scene where Jesus meets the devil in the wilderness, the devil was wearing a cowl, a hood, and when Satan lifted up his head to look at Jesus, it looked like BARAK OBAMA! He remembered how this started a controversy and they removed the character!

This was prophetic and supernatural! Jesus had looked through time and told us of a worldwide tv show where Barak Obama would be revealed as Satan, and this would reveal to us in real life that Barak Obama would have the character of Satan, and be an earthly impression of the anti-Christ.

"It's all starting to come together now!" Micah said out loud. "When Barak Obama was given the nod by the Democratic Party, he had a special platform made for him to speak from! He had it set on the 50 yard line on Invesco Field in Mile High Stadium in Denver, Colorado!"

Of course, Micah thought, *on a high place!*

He began to research this special stage that was built for Barak Obama, and when he saw it, it stunned him! But there it was, and it could not be denied. It was THE THRONE OF PERGAMON, THE THRONE OF Satan! It was almost an exact replica of the throne of Satan in Berlin, Germany! It had not been raised since the days of Hitler! *My God,* Micah thought, *this plan is deep and is being executed in a very real and strategic way!*

Satan's throne had been raised again, unbeknown to most of Gods people! Micah looked at the picture of the platform Barak Obama spoke from in Mile High Stadium, and it almost perfectly fit over the top of the throne of Pergamon in Berlin!

Micah remembered how Barak Obama rose up from the middle of it. Micah noticed how the American flag was placed at almost every column around the stage. The Holy Ghost dropped into Micah's heart, the prophecy in Isaiah the 14th chapter, where Satan said I will exalt MY THRONE ABOVE THE STARS OF God! America was raised up because we loved God! The flag of The United States is The Stars and Stripes, now here was literally the Throne of Satan exalted above the stars of God!

Why did we not see? Micah thought, *here it is! Now since Gods people did not anoint McCain as President, and Barack Obama won the election.*

Micah began to reason, "The Cycle was altered severely and could change eternity!"

Of course, Micah thought, *Satan has manipulated this cycle! Because the modern Jehu, John McCain, was not elected, and because he was not elected then Jehu's chariots was not there to run, politically, over Jezebel when she was thrown down! My God, Micah thought, Satan gained access to the future! After the Jehu of old became the king of Israel, they had peace, 28 years of peace. Since John McCain was not elected, prophetically those 28 years was set into limbo, and it actually threw us 28 years into the future! 28 is the number of eternity!*

No wonder, Micah thought, *people don't know what to do in these times! It's no wonder they're so confused! These events with Barack Obama were not supposed to happen for another 28 years! My God, Micah thought. Oh Lord God, in Jesus Name help us Lord! Show me what I can do! Only God's people have* the power to move time, like Hezekiah and Joshua of old. The devil does not have the power to move time, unless he can get the Body of Christ to do it for him!

"God's people did give it to him!" Micah just said right out loud. "They did it when they did not elect the modern Jehu, John McCain! Satan for the first time we know of is operating 28 Years in the future!"

He's ahead of the light, Micah thought! *By Gods people giving him their light in the future, he has actually transformed himself into an angel of light! Satan is leading Gods people FROM BE-HIND, CONTROLLING THE FUTURE! This is the spirit,* Micah thought, *operating in Barak Obama. He leads from behind!*

"28 is the NUMBER OF ETERNITY!" Micah said. "The enemy was given something that will allow him to manipulate eternity! YHVH means He who lives in eternity! This seizing of 28 years could allow the enemy to operate in eternity!"

Micah stopped and prayed: "Father in Jesus name, show me his plan. What could the enemy possibly be planning to do with these 28 years?"

It seemed now that Micah was moving in high gear! It was like since 2008 God's people had their heads in a bag shouting, but no one could hear!

The Intel was all starting to make sense now: November 28, 2013, Chanukah and Thanksgiving fell on the same day! From that day it was 28 days until the celebration of Christmas! 28 the number of eternity. There was a 28 day portal open to declare every day for 28 days into the future!

November 28, 2013, was also the anniversary of something very few knew of. In the 13th century, a comet called called Negra passed by the sun and the earth, and then the Black Death hit the earth! 666 years from then is November 28, 2013, the comet ISON passed by the sun and the earth. After the comet Ison another black death arose, its name was "ISIS!" The worst terrorist group the modern world had ever seen! Barak Obama played them down and let them proliferate!

What was so particular about this group however was the fact that they came in the year 666 after the first Black Death hit! Then 2013, 2+0+1+3 = 6 it was the year of the 6! The group, Isis, wear bandanas around their foreheads, that actually have words on them that say "In the name of Allah!" This phrase on the foreheads of these terrorist is almost identical to three greek letters that actually stand for numbers , and those numbers are 666!

No wonder John said in Revelation 13:8 "Here is wisdom. Let him that hath understanding count the number of the beast: for it is the number of a man; and his number is Six hundred three score and six" John understanding greek understood this when he saw the letters! The terrorist group Isis they also wear a cuff around their right arm that has the same three greek letters on them, 666, and they behead Christians and Jews!

The Holy Ghost began to put all the pieces of the puzzle together for Micah. The Mighty Holy Ghost had showed Micah years earlier that there's always the image of an event in the earth, before the event arrives!

God created Adam's spirit first, then he formed Adams body from the dust of the earth. The LORD God then breathed into Adams nostrils the spirit He had created. So there was the image of a man in the earth, (his body) before the spirit of the man arrived! This would always be the precedent! There would always be the image of the thing that was coming to the earth before the thing arrives; because there has to be a body in its image in order to hold it!

This is why 911 was so familiar, Micah thought. *After the towers were hit, Rudy Juliani made a biblical statement, when he said, "New York, New York what city is like this great city?" This verse is from the book of Revelation chapter 18 speaking of Babylon, the trade capital of the world!*

Everything happened just like this, the city was hit in one hour and the ship masters watched the smoke of her burning from the sea! They watched it from the harbor! This was a perfect body of the time of tribulation to come! It formed the body of the event! This is why the Prophetic Camp kept saying it's the tribulation time! They were confusing the body of the event with the actual event to come! And now with Barack Obama, there was a body of the anti-Christ to come! It was all falling into place! Someone knew all of this but the majority of the body of Christ sure didn't!

Chapter 6

The Ta-Wer

"Shut up you fool!" Sä·na' had seemed to go into an uncontrollable rage as he raked a creature up with his talons.

This smaller winged creature had spoken up and said, "I will have a special position in the earth also!"

"You're nothing!" Sä·na' yelled, as his talons ripped into him again, the creature was screaming obscenities! The demonic beings were excited and began sounding like wild animals watching Sä·na' rip into the lower ranking angel!

"You don't know anything," Sä·na' said, "and you'll never be anything!"

To the creatures relief, Sä·na' suddenly stormed out of the room leaving the injured fallen being whimpering on the floor, cursing and swearing. It is hard on these cursed beings when they are injured, they never recover and yet they can never die! Therefore they are forced to bear the pain for eternity!

Suddenly there was a low whirring sound and the great lid began to rattle! Everything in the underworld grew quiet as if all of them were anticipating something to happen.

Sä·na' stopped and listened intently to the low whirring sound coming from the other side of the great lid. He flew wildly up toward the great lid while the others stood in silence watching him.

He flew into the lid violently! He was pushing against it trying to help open it from the underside! Sä·na' suddenly stopped, and put his ear up against the underside of the lid, listening. "I know that sound," Sä·na' said with a sinister tone. "It's the Ta-Wer! I haven't heard it that strong in a long time!" He kept pushing against it, slamming himself in desperation to get the lid open!

Sä·na' was partly right in that it was like the Ta-Wer. However, what the fallen creature did not know was that on the other side of that lid was a great underground scientific facility, CERN. The whirring sound he was hearing was not the old Ta-Wer; it was the giant Hadron Collider built in Switzerland over the old temple of Apollo!

It did, however, do the same job in that it could open a portal to another dimension. A modern version of the Ta-Wer, only much more powerful!

Sä·na' stopped slamming into the great lid and got quiet. While he was clinging to it, he began listening more intently. It was quiet, all but the low whirring sound and the occasional sloshing of the damned souls in the pool. Sä·na' flew back down. "It won't be long now," he said to the others.

At the same time on the other side of the lid at CERN, a conversation was going on between top ranking scientists:

****

Intelligence Data:

> Scientist over each department at CERN collectively, are referred to as "The Family." Father is the chief scientist in

charge. Mother is the next in command.

****

"We need to get this thing up to full power by Sept 23rd; the portal must open by then," Mother said.

"Why then?" A scientist asked.

"Because, this time we have everything in place!" Mother said with excitement.

"But what if it causes another earthquake, or worse?"

"It won't matter this time," Mother said. "The family has waited a long time to open this portal, and by Apollo we will open it! What do you think all the nations have funded us for? They think we're hunting energy, but we will open the great Lid! The portal will be opened and Apollo will be able to return! We have fed the public one narrative but you, me, and the rest of the scientist here know differently. Listen, it's like Father said, we do this in the name of science, and the governments fund it all in the name of greed!"

"Yes, Mother," the scientist replied, "but you know what happened to Father the last time we almost came up to full power!"

"I know" Mother replied, "but it was a sacrifice for science."

The scientist was very uneasy. For the last time they tried to open the portal, father went missing. Father finally appeared again, but no one knows exactly what happened to him.

Chapter 7

Madonna, The Pope & CERN!

The Lord had spoken to Micah about the calendar. It looked as if September 2015 was a target date for something. Micah had knowledge of CERN and what they were trying to do. The giant Hadron Collider was built over the ancient temple of Apollo. On the property, an idol of Shiva, the false god of destruction, was erected. Not long ago, a human sacrifice at CERN was caught on video late at night. Although the incident was played down as a prank, one has to ask the question why it was done at all. CERN had tried to open the portal more than once and had some success, but had not yet achieved what they wanted.

As they opened the portal a little at a time, they saw faces of hideous creatures appear in the open door. The scientists there desperately wanted to bring them over to this dimension! One would wonder what those Satanic scientists would have done if they had known that one of the faces they were seeing was the face of Sä·na' as he slammed himself into the lid. The other vague faces were all the others gathered behind Sä·na', trying to see the other side of the great lid!

The plan of Satan had never changed over all these years. Children are the heritage of the LORD, and the abortion of these babies turned whole mindsets away from God. A river of blood had been offered to Satan in the temples called abortion clinics! This blood of the innocent babies has degenerated some of the human minds until now they'll do anything with no moral conscience. A society that can kill their own children is capable of any sin they can imagine! And this is what Satan needed to access the imagination of men.

Science is always the first to deny God and the spirit world; however, they know it is all very real! Both the narrative "There is no God" that is being spread all over the world, and the killing of God's heritage are being funded by the same groups.

Without realizing it, people are being herded like cattle into a pen!

The scientist at CERN learned that the reason they could not get the great lid opened was because even though they had the science, they needed the religious ritual. They also needed the spiritual authority of a man recognized by the authority of the collective of man, like The President!

Micah began to notice this pattern pointing toward September 2015.

French Minister of Foreign Affairs, Laurent Fabius, standing with John Kerry on May 13, 2014, made an international statement that we as a planet only had 500 days to avoid a great climate chaos! 500 days from that announcement is September 24, 2015!

Different self-proclaimed members of the illuminati had said that after September, things would change.

"Wait a minute!" Micah exclaimed "Is this why we've seen Madonna (a long time blasphemer of all that is holy) doing strange things, like performing ancient Occult type rituals on stage, while dressed in clothing that resembled some kind of high priestess? Hold on, Madonna's Rebel Heart tour and her opening theme is literally called, "Desecration of The Bride", and "Arrival of Fallen Angels"!

"Well," Micah said to himself, "look at that. Madonna's tour begins September this year! Is she trying to reintroduce the Nephilim by performing ancient rituals?

Micah quickly looked at his bullet points:

• Madonna is going to perform these rituals at Madison Square Garden Sept 16, 2015.

• The Pope will come to Madison Square Garden September 25, 2015

• Madonna is going to perform these rituals in Philadelphia Sept 24, 2015

• The Pope will be in Philadelphia September 26, 2015.

• The Pope is coming to address the American Congress September 24, 2015

• He is also holding Holy Mass with The World Meetings of The Families September 26, 2015!

"Wherever the Madonna goes, The Pope goes!"

"This also explains the giant binocular telescope owned by the Vatican on Mt. Graham!" "This telescope has an infrared camera named Lucifer!" Micah exclaimed. Micah knew that The Catholic Church had been looking for extra-terrestrials for years from there. The Catholic hierarchy said that they were already among us.

"They all know! My God," Micah said, "they all know! This world is about to be totally taken off guard." Micah knew there was only about 30 days left to stop it. The government's plot was to execute this plan in September 2015. CERN was set to open the portal to another dimension on September 23, 2015

"They have figured it out!" Micah shouted. "They are going to open the portal and bring these fallen beings from the other side!"

"Of course," Micah said, "the Mayan prophecy wasn't the end in 2012, it was the beginning of something in 2012!"

Micah grabbed a one dollar bill out of his wallet and looked at the pyramid on the back of it.

"The roman numerals at the bottom, 1776," Micah said. "It began here! 13 steps to the top of the pyramid, 13 Katun or Mayan cycles, approximately 20 years each! Then the eye of Apollo or the return of Apollo, not in 2012, but it will begin in 2012! That's the second term of Barak Obama!"

"Let's see," Micah said to himself. "Barak Obama, no birth certificate, and everyone that knows him swears he is from Africa."

"Wait a minute!" Micah exclaimed out loud. "Africa!"

Micah reached for his Bible. Quickly, he opened it to Isaiah 46:9-10:

9 Remember the former things of old: for I am God, and there is none else; I am God, and there is none like me,

10 Declaring the end from the beginning, and from ancient times the things that are not yet done, saying, My counsel shall stand, and I will do all my pleasure:

Micah read it again, but this time out loud, *"Declaring the end from the beginning, and from ancient times the things that are not yet done"*

Following this simple formula and taking God at His Word it was very clear to Micah.

"Genesis is the book of beginnings," Micah said. "Therefore taking God at His Word the end must be declared from there! Reading Genesis forward is actually reading Revelation Backward!"

Micah began to go over the order of the future concerning the closing of the age.

- End of the Church Age

- Catching away or the rapture of the church

- The Tribulation Period

- The end of the Tribulation Period when Jesus returns and defeats the anti-Christ

- The 1,000 year Millennial Reign of Christ

- Then Satan will be loosed for a little season again to tempt the nations

- Satan is defeated and is cast into the lake of fire and brimstone where the beast and the false prophet are

- Then everything is put back into its rightful order and the scripture says that the Son give all things back to His Father and God will be All in All

"This is the order," Micah said, "therefore we should be able to find this in Genesis."

"Here it is," Micah said to himself, "Genesis chapter 7, the flood of Noah, the end of an age!" Micah continued to go backward and he found it all!

Genesis 5, Enoch was caught away! A rapture!

Genesis 4, Cain killed Abel, That's the Tribulation Period! A man with a mark killing a man without a mark.

Genesis 3,The seed of the woman will crush the enemy's head. This is the end of the tribulation.

Genesis 2. The Garden of Eden! A perfect paradise! This would be The Millennial Reign of Christ!

Genesis 1:2 And the earth was without form and void and darkness was upon the face of the deep.

"Darkness upon the face of the deep," Micah said, "this would be Satan being loosed for a little season again, and the earth becomes chaotic!"

Genesis 1:1 In the beginning God!

"After all of these events, Satan, the beast, and the false prophet are all thrown into the lake of fire forever, and God is once again all in all! "The exact pattern" Micah said.

Then Micah began to look at Genesis 2: 9-14:

9 And out of the ground made the LORD God to grow every tree that is pleasant to the sight, and good for food; the tree of life also in the midst of the garden, and the tree of knowledge of good and evil.

10 And a river went out of Eden to water the garden; and from thence it was parted, and be-came into four heads.

11 The name of the first is Pison: that is it which compasseth the whole land of Havilah, where there is gold;

12 And the gold of that land is good: there is bdellium and the onyx stone.

13 And the name of the second river is Gihon: the same is it that compasseth the whole land of Ethiopia.

14 And the name of the third river is <u>Hiddekel</u>: that is it which goeth toward the east of Assyria. And the fourth river is <u>Euphrates</u>.

Micah, prompted by the Holy Ghost, took the names: <u>Pison</u>, <u>Havilah</u>, <u>Gihon</u>, <u>Ethiopia</u>, <u>Hiddekel</u>, <u>Assyria</u>, <u>Euphrates</u>. He took the meanings and put them together. As he translated these names, he read them out loud: "In the gushing forth, in the rushing forth, there will arise a powerful son of Cushi, a black man having great authority."

"This man will arise," Micah pondered. "But it will be in the time of the gushing, and the rushing forth. Rushing forth has to do with time," Micah said. "In the gushing forth, in the rushing forth of time, this powerful son of Cushi will appear! Cushi, from Africa, this man will be of African descent! This is Barak Obama!" Micah said. "His father is from Kenya and he is the leader of the most powerful nation in the world!"

Now the rushing forth of time, Micah thought, *the rushing forth of time,* he thought again, *what could that mean?*

Chapter 8

The Calendar!

Micah was sitting in church when suddenly the Holy Ghost prompted him to look at the calendar; it was 2015. "Sum The Year: the Spirit of God said to him.

Micah obeyed; 2+0+1+5=8 *Yes a new beginning,* Micah thought. Then The Spirit of God said to Micah, "Now sum the whole calendar years starting from the year 2000." Micah did and something astonishing took place:

2	3	4	5	6	7	8
2000 = 2	2010 = 3	2020 = 4	2030 = 5	2040 = 6	2050 = 7	2060 = 8
2001 = 3	2011 = 4	2021 = 5	2031 = 6	2041 = 7	2051 = 8	2061 = 9
2002 = 4	2012 = 5	2022 = 6	2032 = 7	2042 = 8	2052 = 9	2062 = 10
2003 = 5	2013 = 6	2023 = 7	2033 = 8	2043 = 9	2053 = 10	2063 = 11
2004 = 6	2014 = 7	2024 = 8	2034 = 9	2044 = 10	2054 = 11	2064 = 12
2005 = 7	2015 = 8	2025 = 9	2035 = 10	2045 = 11	2055 = 12	2065 = 13
2006 = 8	2016 = 9	2026 = 10	2036 = 11	2046 = 12	2056 = 13	2066 = 14
2007 = 9	2017 = 10	2027 = 11	2037 = 12	2047 = 13	2057 = 14	2067 = 15
2008 = 10	2018 = 11	2028 = 12	2038 = 13	2048 = 14	2058 = 15	2068 = 16
2009 = 11	2019 = 12	2029 = 13	2039 = 14	2049 = 15	2059 = 16	2069 = 17

It wasn't long before he noticed that the numbers were in consecutive order vertically. Column 1 starting with 2 through 11, then after 11, the sequence would break and begin again at the top of the next column with 3 and goes vertically through

12! It followed suit and Micah continued this through the year 2069. As he looked across the top of the chart, from 2000-2060, the numbers follow suit, 2,3,4,5,6,7,8! It seemed that every 10 years there was a reset! And the top of every reset could represent a day.

Now, the chart got stranger by the moment. Starting with the year 2000 the sum of 2, going down diagonally, you begin counting by 2's 2000 = 2, 2011=4, 2022=6 and 2033=8, not only going down diagonally are you counting by 2's,

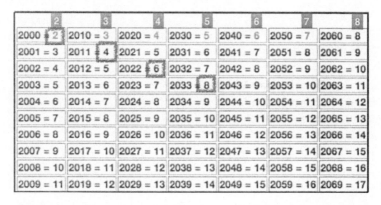

but it does the same thing with every number going down the chart. Start at three diagonally, your counting by 2's, such as 3,5,7,9, and so forth.

2	3	4	5	6	7	8
2000 = 2	2010 = 3	2020 = 4	2030 = 5	2040 = 6	2050 = 7	2060 = 8
2001 = 3	2011 = 4	2021 = 5	2031 = 6	2041 = 7	2051 = 8	2061 = 9
2002 = 4	2012 = 5	2022 = 6	2032 = 7	2042 = 8	2052 = 9	2062 = 10
2003 = 5	2013 = 6	2023 = 7	2033 = 8	2043 = 9	2053 = 10	2063 = 11
2004 = 6	2014 = 7	2024 = 8	2034 = 9	2044 = 10	2054 = 11	2064 = 12
2005 = 7	2015 = 8	2025 = 9	2035 = 10	2045 = 11	2055 = 12	2065 = 13
2006 = 8	2016 = 9	2026 = 10	2036 = 11	2046 = 12	2056 = 13	2066 = 14
2007 = 9	2017 = 10	2027 = 11	2037 = 12	2047 = 13	2057 = 14	2067 = 15
2008 = 10	2018 = 11	2028 = 12	2038 = 13	2048 = 14	2058 = 15	2068 = 16
2009 = 11	2019 = 12	2029 = 13	2039 = 14	2049 = 15	2059 = 16	2069 = 17

"Why would we start from the year 2000?" Micah asks.

The Lord reminded him of the story of the Good Samaritan. This certain man was traveling from Jerusalem to Jericho and fell among thieves. They stripped him of his raiment and wounded him-leaving him half dead. A certain priest came by, saw him, and passed by on the other side. Likewise, a Levite saw him and passed by on the other side. But a certain Samaritan in his journeys came by, saw him, and had compassion on him. He poured in oil and wine, bound up his wounds, and took him to the inn. The Samaritan gave the inn keeper two pence or two days wages, and said to the Inn keeper, take care of him and if it is more than this, I will pay you when I return.

The Certain man was Adam who used to live in Jerusalem. He left his home there and went down to Jericho. The ancient Jewish teachers taught that Satan's throne used to sit on the moon. The name Jericho in Hebrew means "Moon." On his way down there to "The Moon," Adam fell among thieves. But one of the translations in Greek is "fell in" with thieves or "lighted" among them! Adam committed treason; the scripture declares that the woman was deceived, the man was not. Adam joined these thieves. They stripped him of his raiment; the Glory of God that used to cover him, and wounded him-leaving him half dead. Before this, Adam only knew good. But after this, he knew both good and evil; he became half dead!

The Priesthood couldn't save him, the Levitical Law couldn't save him, but a certain Samaritan came to him in his journeys. A Samaritan is a man who is a half Jew; a man whose mother is Jewish but his father is something else. Jesus' mother was Jewish, but His Father was God! Jesus was the Samaritan in the story! He took the man and poured in oil, the anointing of God, and wine, the Blood of Jesus! The Samaritan then took the man to the place of comfort and gave him to the Comforter, or the Holy Ghost to keep him until he returned. One of the keys here is that the Samaritan gave the inn keeper two pence, or two days wages!

Now 2 Peter 3:8 says; "One day is with the Lord is as a 1,000 years and a 1,000 years is as one day" The inn keeper received two days wages or enough to keep the man for 2,000 YEARS! Until His return, He said if he was any longer in returning, He would pay it when He returned! This not only gives us the time line of 2000 years but also the ability to make it longer. So in the calendar, in the year 2000, we begin.

Micah drew out the summed prophetic calendar so he could begin to study it. Micah took the 28 years that the enemy got hold of because the body of Christ did not elect John McCain as President. Micah then applied this 28 years to the prophetic calendar. He started from the time Barak Obama was elected president. When he did, something very interesting happened!

President Barak Obama was elected in 2008, but officially took office Jan 20, 2009. So therefore, we're dealing with two dates 2008 & 2009. Beginning at 2008, counting 28 years into the future, this would throw us into the year 2035! But from the official date he took office in Jan 2009, 28 years would be 2036!

Micah circled the dates on the prophetic calendar.

2	3	4	5	6	7	8
2000 = 2	2010 = 3	2020 = 4	2030 = 5	2040 = 6	2050 = 7	2060 = 8
2001 = 3	2011 = 4	2021 = 5	2031 = 6	2041 = 7	2051 = 8	2061 = 9
2002 = 4	2012 = 5	2022 = 6	2032 = 7	2042 = 8	2052 = 9	2062 = 10
2003 = 5	2013 = 6	2023 = 7	2033 = 8	2043 = 9	2053 = 10	2063 = 11
2004 = 6	2014 = 7	2024 = 8	2034 = 9	2044 = 10	2054 = 11	2064 = 12
2005 = 7	2015 = 8	2025 = 9	2035 = 10	2045 = 11	2055 = 12	2065 = 13
2006 = 8	2016 = 9	2026 = 10	2036 = 11	2046 = 12	2056 = 13	2066 = 14
2007 = 9	2017 = 10	2027 = 11	2037 = 12	2047 = 13	2057 = 14	2067 = 15
2008 = 10	2018 = 11	2028 = 12	2038 = 13	2048 = 14	2058 = 15	2068 = 16
2009 = 11	2019 = 12	2029 = 13	2039 = 14	2049 = 15	2059 = 16	2069 = 17

In legal time, 2,000 years after Jesus arose from the dead would be somewhere around 2030! If Jesus was set to return in 2030 for The Rapture of The Church, then "2036, would put us at the end of the tribulation period!" The dates puts it past the Rapture date!

Now Micah knew he might not have these dates to the exact, but it was sure legally close, and the devil is a legal devil! But what about the four dates?

Micah began to notice that If you look at the chart and look at the sums 2000 = 2, 2010=3, 2011= 4, but, 2001 also = 3, and 2011 = 4. Therefore, 2000, 2010, and 2011 is 2, 3 and 4, half of a square. Then the other half of the same square 2000, 2001 and 2011 is also 2, 3 and 4! Or you could say 2, 3, and 4 both ways seals it like a cube!

Ezekiel 28 tells us Satan seals up "The Sum! Wait a minute, here it is! This is why there is four dates. This is on purpose! The enemy's going to cube time! Satan is going to try and seal up the sum!

2	3	4	5	6	7	8
2000 = 2	2010 = 3	2020 = 4	2030 = 5	2040 = 6	2050 = 7	2060 = 8
2001 = 3	2011 = 4	2021 = 5	2031 = 6	2041 = 7	2051 = 8	2061 = 9
2002 = 4	2012 = 5	2022 = 6	2032 = 7	2042 = 8	2052 = 9	2062 = 10
2003 = 5	2013 = 6	2023 = 7	2033 = 8	2043 = 9	2053 = 10	2063 = 11
2004 = 6	2014 = 7	2024 = 8	2034 = 9	2044 = 10	2054 = 11	2064 = 12
2005 = 7	2015 = 8	2025 = 9	2035 = 10	2045 = 11	2055 = 12	2065 = 13
2006 = 8	2016 = 9	2026 = 10	2036 = 11	2046 = 12	2056 = 13	2066 = 14
2007 = 9	2017 = 10	2027 = 11	2037 = 12	2047 = 13	2057 = 14	2067 = 15
2008 = 10	2018 = 11	2028 = 12	2038 = 13	2048 = 14	2058 = 15	2068 = 16
2009 = 11	2019 = 12	2029 = 13	2039 = 14	2049 = 15	2059 = 16	2069 = 17

2	3	4	5	6	7	8
2000 = 2	2010 = 3	2020 = 4	2030 = 5	2040 = 6	2050 = 7	2060 = 8
2001 = 3	2011 = 4	2021 = 5	2031 = 6	2041 = 7	2051 = 8	2061 = 9
2002 = 4	2012 = 5	2022 = 6	2032 = 7	2042 = 8	2052 = 9	2062 = 10
2003 = 5	2013 = 6	2023 = 7	2033 = 8	2043 = 9	2053 = 10	2063 = 11
2004 = 6	2014 = 7	2024 = 8	2034 = 9	2044 = 10	2054 = 11	2064 = 12
2005 = 7	2015 = 8	2025 = 9	2035 = 10	2045 = 11	2055 = 12	2065 = 13
2006 = 8	2016 = 9	2026 = 10	2036 = 11	2046 = 12	2056 = 13	2066 = 14
2007 = 9	2017 = 10	2027 = 11	2037 = 12	2047 = 13	2057 = 14	2067 = 15
2008 = 10	2018 = 11	2028 = 12	2038 = 13	2048 = 14	2058 = 15	2068 = 16
2009 = 11	2019 = 12	2029 = 13	2039 = 14	2049 = 15	2059 = 16	2069 = 17

"But why cube these dates?" Micah pondered.

Then it started to become more clear him. The calendar was a man's calendar and the Number of a man, is 6.

Wait a minute, Micah thought, looking at the summed calendar. *2008 and 2009 are the years Barak Obama became President.* So Micah drew a line from 2008, to 2009. He then made a square with these years and the surrounding years: 2018 and 2019. Micah started to add the numbers in each year: 2+0+0+8=10, 2+0+1+8=11, and 2+0+1+9=12. 10,11, and 12. *Interesting,* Micah thought. Micah then added the digits in each of those numbers: 1+0=1, 1+1=2, and 1+2=3. *1,2, and 3,* Micah thought. *1+2+3=6!* He looked at this some more. *This works the same using the other half of this square! Micah thought to himself. Using this same process but using the years 2008, 2009, and 2019 still equals 6!*

Hmm, Micah thought, Then when Micah looked at the year 2035 he got by adding the 28 lost years from 2008.

"The cube here," Micah said, "is 2035=10, 2036=11, 2046=12. 10=1, 11=2, 12=3! or 1, 2,3! or 1+2+3 which also equals 6. Going the other way 2035 - 2045 - 2046 adds down to the same number 6.

There it is, Micah thought, *cube one is 6, Cube two is 6, which is 66. Then if you follow the summed calendar from 2046 to the top of the calendar it is on day 6!*

"Well, Well," Micah said out loud. "Look at that! 666!"

2	3	4	5	6	7	8
2000 = 2	2010 = 3	2020 = 4	2030 = 5	2040 = 6	2050 = 7	2060 = 8
2001 = 3	2011 = 4	2021 = 5	2031 = 6	2041 = 7	2051 = 8	2061 = 9
2002 = 4	2012 = 5	2022 = 6	2032 = 7	2042 = 8	2052 = 9	2062 = 10
2003 = 5	2013 = 6	2023 = 7	2033 = 8	2043 = 9	2053 = 10	2063 = 11
2004 = 6	2014 = 7	2024 = 8	2034 = 9	2044 = 10	2054 = 11	2064 = 12
2005 = 7	2015 = 8	2025 = 9	2035 = 10	2045 = 11	2055 = 12	2065 = 13
2006 = 8	2016 = 9	2026 = 10	2036 = 11	2046 = 12	2056 = 13	2066 = 14
2007 = 9	2017 = 10	2027 = 11	2037 = 12	2047 = 13	2057 = 14	2067 = 15
2008 = 10	2018 = 11	2028 = 12	2038 = 13	2048 = 14	2058 = 15	2068 = 16
2009 = 11	2019 = 12	2029 = 13	2039 = 14	2049 = 15	2059 = 16	2069 = 17

"Of course!" Micah said. "The devil is a scientist, an angelic calculator, he understands what makes the tides come in and go out. He does not have love in him, yet through his position as an Archangel (preparing the earth for the man), he knows how numbers and time works in the earth."

****

Intelligence Data:

The devil is a legal devil. After the fall of man, in the definition of Hebrew words, it was re-vealed that man was then caught in the corner where seed and harvest meet. Bound under the law, this is why Jesus' first coming in the fullness of time could be determined by legal time.

Jesus was sent in the fullness of time, but to where was not known by the devil because the devil cannot have revelation knowledge. There's no light in the devil. He has to hear the church preach to learn the manifold wisdom of God (Ephesians 3:10). This is why he had to get Herod to ask the scribes to find the location of Jesus' birth for him in the Word of God.

Herod stopped looking for Him because he thought he killed him in Bethlehem. Then John the Baptist started preaching about the one coming after him. Satan then realized he hadn't killed him in Bethlehem! That he still had The Christ to deal with.

The first coming of Jesus could be calculated by the devil. However, the scripture declares that Christ has redeemed us from the curse of the law, this includes legal time. Therefore, after His resurrection, His return does not have to be determined by any set time! This is revealed to us in the story of the Good Samaritan; He tells the inn keeper here is enough for two days, if I am any longer in my coming I will pay you when I get here!

Now, even though His coming this time in the rapture of the church cannot be calculated to the moment in time by the law, the math still legally sets it to be at a certain time. That time keeps getting suspended by grace and love, and the hunger of the body of Christ. The Father knows when Jesus will come because His return is determined by love and in love, and God is love!

****

If the math, Micah thought, *points to the Church being raptured around 2030, then 2035, 2036, 28 years into the future would put us at the end of the seven year tribulation period, following the Rapture! And if time was sealed at 2036, it then cubes at 2046. And if each number at the top of the chart represents a day then the bottom right corner of the cube would be into the 6th day!*

"By manipulating time this way, the enemy could go beyond the rapture date!"

"The enemy already has a body of the anti-Christ in the earth" Micah pondered. *"Barak Obama! There is a body of the false prophet, which would be the 112th Pope, there is an an Image of the beast, Islam, the great whore of Revelation, Hillary Clinton, and an army to destroy Israel called Isis"*

"Hold it!" Micah spoke out loud. Micah turned to the prophetic calendar again. He began to draw on the calendar connecting dates. By connecting the two squares The Holy Spirit revealed something remarkable to Micah, It made a corridor! A hallway through time!

2	3	4	5	6	7	8
2000 = 2	2010 = 3	2020 = 4	2030 = 5	2040 = 6	2050 = 7	2060 = 8
2001 = 3	2011 = 4	2021 = 5	2031 = 6	2041 = 7	2051 = 8	2061 = 9
2002 = 4	2012 = 5	2022 = 6	2032 = 7	2042 = 8	2052 = 9	2062 = 10
2003 = 5	2013 = 6	2023 = 7	2033 = 8	2043 = 9	2053 = 10	2063 = 11
2004 = 6	2014 = 7	2024 = 8	2034 = 9	2044 = 10	2054 = 11	2064 = 12
2005 = 7	2015 = 8	2025 = 9	2035 = 10	= 11	2055 = 12	2065 = 13
2006 = 8	2016 = 9	2026 = 10	2036 = 11	= 12	2056 = 13	2066 = 14
2007 = 9	2017 = 10	2027 = 11	2037 = 12	2047 = 13	2057 = 14	2067 = 15
2008 = 10	2018 = 11	2028 = 12	2038 = 13	2048 = 14	2058 = 15	2068 = 16
2009 = 11	2019 = 12	2029 = 13	2039 = 14	2049 = 15	2059 = 16	2069 = 17

"If Satan could walk through time past the time of the rapture, let the spirit that will possess the anti-Christ back into the now, he would force the rapture of the Church to take place. Then the Christians that chose to believe in the pre-tribulation Rapture, which are "the restrainers," would leave! Then the only Christians left here will be those here by choice!" *But,* Micah pondered. *In the time after the Rapture, the Grace age has ended and Israel is then the focus. Animal sacrifice would begin again and basically the world will go back under the law, because Gods attention is now focused on Israel.*

The Tribulation Micah thought. *Is a massive harvest, Satan is an angel with the right to gather mens harvest. He could lay violent hold on the power of the believers that choose to stay here, and use it! He could open the bottomless pit, loose the hoards upon the earth, and with the sixth day sealed he would never have to leave, the great tribulation would go on forever! There would be no everlasting punishment for him, he would have made God's Word not come to pass, thereby using God's own Word to once again, like in the world before Adam, legally hang the world and reign by death in the earth!*

* *

Intelligence Data:

> The Abyss is a prison and Satan is the king over it. It would be like Al Capone with all of his minions in Alcatraz. If he could break them out of prison all at once he just might be unstoppable! Satan already has a hoard of demons on the earth. If he couples those in the earth with those he breaks out of prison, he could create a hybrid race of people and his dream of becoming flesh covered crimson would then be realized! To do this he must have Christians by their OWN CHOICE here during the tribulation, in order to seize on their power. just like Genesis 6: And they took them wives all of whom THEY CHOSE!

> The enemy is using the authority of the body of Christ to do this! This shows just how much authority the body of Christ has.

* *

"The enemy is actually in position to do it," Micah said out loud. "and the body of Christ never saw it coming!"

Chapter 9

The Ranch

The Lord had risen up a stronghold for the Kingdom of God in the remote mountains of Idaho. A man had caught hold of the vision of saving Gods people during the tribulation period. He was preparing to sustain at least 50,000 people for seven years. He came from a very wealthy family and he was radically turned on to Jesus Christ!

Unbeknownst to Micah, this man had been getting CDs of Micah's teaching and was compelled to have him come and speak at a prophetic conference at his ranch. The conference was filled with prophets from various places. Knowledge was out that after September 23rd, 2015 all hell was going to break loose.

A lot of the watchmen (The Prophetic Stream of the body of Christ) were convinced that there was no way to avoid it. Satan had brought a great deception to them. The watchmen are too powerful to be overcome by a straight out frontal attack, therefore it must be by a very subtle plan of deception.

Satan had convinced a lot of the prophetic stream that the pre-tribulation Rapture of the church was not real and to preach a pre-tribulation Rapture was in error. For this reason a lot of the powerful prophets did not use their anointing to act in any way as if a pre-tribulation Rapture was going to happen. The enemy had nullified their faith in this promise, therefore, the people primarily responsible for being watchmen on the wall were now confused as to what was coming.

* *

Intelligence Data:

> The revelation of God being Absolutely Good must be embraced before the prophetic can be seen clearly. The prophetic is like deep pools of dark mysteries that roll with waves of time. It is imperative that God be seen as Absolutely Good in order to see these mysteries and set these times. God never causes bad, He never allows bad in the causative sense, He never uses pain to teach, and He never ever kills! One must never waver from this knowledge in order to discover the great mysteries of the deep waters and find the cause of what is happening, and why it's happening. Then and only then, can one set these things in their proper time.

> When God created man He created the man's spirit first, then He formed the man's body, then breathed the man's spirit into his body. The name Man is speaking of the spirit, while human or humous refers to the body. This is what human beings are; "humous-men," or "spirits in dirt" or "Humans!" There was an image of the man in the earth (man's body) before the man arrived! This is the forever precedent! There will always be an image of the event coming in the earth before the event arrives! If one does not know this, then the images of the event could easily be confused with the actual event yet to come!

> Knowing this precedent, the enemy further strengthened his deception in the prophets by confusing them on the prophetic times. For if there is no pre-tribulation Rapture, you would never think there could possibly be impressions

in the earth of a coming event, for one would confuse the impressions for the actual event! If this occurs, then you find yourself fighting flesh and blood and that is not the real enemy. For we wrestle not against flesh and blood, but against principalities, powers, rulers of the darkness of this world, against spiritual wickedness in high or heavenly places. If one is blindsided fighting flesh and blood, the real power which is the spirit of that body, can arrive undetected and attack from behind!

* *

Meetings were being called by the Spirit of God! All anyone knew was that they were urgent!

Micah could sense this urgency in his spirit.

In the month of April two such gatherings took place among the watchmen. Both were in Idaho USA. The Western United States is pivotal in the kingdom. The United States of America is laid out in the order of the Tabernacle Moses built.

If you take a clear plastic overlay of the Tabernacle and a U.S map the same size, and lay the overlay of the Tabernacle on top of the U.S map, something rather amazing takes place that does not happen this way with any other nation's map!

There are two nations in existence that are unique from all others especially concerning God!

One is Israel. Israel was created because God loved them; the other is America. America was created because we loved God! The two nations that blatantly show the Agape of God are now on the earth at the same time!

The Tabernacle was given to man through Israel, and the

Tabernacle is actually seen in the lay out of the United States of America!

Micah began to look at this. You entered the Tabernacle from the east and moved toward the west. This in itself prophetically shows that in the natural, the Tabernacle would start in the east and be seen in its finish in the west, showing the Great Agape of God from the east to the west among the nations. In terms of nations, think on this scripture: Psalm 103:12 - As far as the east is from the west, so far has he removed our transgressions from us.

Now as you entered the Tabernacle from the east you first came to the Brazen Altar (Fire), then the Laver (Water), then you entered the inner court, to the left is the Menorah (Oil), to the right is the Table of Shew Bread (Wheat and Grains), straight ahead is the Golden Alter of incense (Red Coals), then in The Holy of Holies is the Golden ark of the Covenant (Gold).

Now if we lay our plastic overlay of the Tabernacle on top of our map of the USA, when the colonist came to the US, they came in through the east coast. The entrance has always been the east coast. In America, just like the Brazen Altar of fire, the first places you come to is where the first fires of revival began to burn in America; Kentucky and North Carolina. The first famous outpouring of the Holy Ghost is recorded in North Carolina. From this, the Christian Union was formed and became the Church of God headquarters in Cleveland, Tennessee!

If you keep moving west you come to the Mississippi River and it would set where the Laver sat in the Tabernacle.

As you move into the Holy Place through the first veil held up by five posts, which represent the five fold ministry, on your left would be the Menorah with its oil. In our overlay, this Oil burning Menorah would be in the Texas, Oklahoma area; the two US major oil producing states! The Menorah was the only light in The Tabernacle! The oil produced in these states is used to produce energy for the rest of the nation.

To the right was the table of Shew Bread. These lands are Kansas, Nebraska and the Dakotas, or "The Bread Basket of America!" As we continue toward the west, we see the Golden Altar of Incense. The Incense used in Moses' time contained 11 different kinds of spices. It had a deep red color to it. The Altar of Incense on our over lay would fall on the state of Colorado which is named after the Colorado River, which was named by the Spanish explorers because it means reddish in color! Colorado is where some of our largest coal deposits are found!

Continuing on, we come to the second veil that leads to The Holy Of Holies! Where God would meet with man! This is where the Ark of the Covenant sat! The veil sits on Americas Continental Divide! This is an imaginary line that marks the highest regions in the country!

Then once past the divide, you come to the Ark of the Covenant, overlaid with pure gold! On the overlay, it sits in the area of California, Oregon, and Washington; three states known for one thing, gold! This is also the place where Trinity Broadcasting Network (TBN) was founded and took the Gospel to the rest of the nation and the world! Also, looking at the overlay, the Holy of Holies also lands on, IDAHO!

These prophetic meetings were being called in the west, in Idaho, or inside The Holy of Holies!

Chapter 10

The Prophets Gather

Micah received his invitation for the major prophetic event in Idaho. He was invited to bring a prophetic team of warriors and minister there. Micah assembled his elite team and they made their way across the U.S

This was a unique time because the meeting was scheduled for the 20th of September.

Micah began to settle in on the airplane contemplating these things.

Every demon in the earth was on high alert! The call had come down through their ranks. Satan's chief lieutenant frantically gave his report to the slothful, arrogant, fallen creature.

"Master," Satan's chief lieutenant reported to him, "there is massive movement in two streams of the separated ones! The Word of Faith stream and the Prophetic stream! The Word of Faith stream is using the force of faith in a magnitude that we haven't seen since before Adam fell! But the most massive deployment of soldiers is coming from The Prophets! They seem to be migrating towards the west, in powerful numbers!"

"Well, of course they are," Satan answered with a merciless voice. "All creation knows that everything is about to change! We have never been more ready for this event than we are now! The delusion is strong enough that some of the seers are not sure of what they are seeing.

"HA! HA," the chief of depravity roared in laughter.

"Yes," the lieutenant responded, "but what about those in the Word of Faith? They keep saying it is not the end that they will win!"

"Yes," Satan answered. "But, I have managed in my awesome planning, to keep the Word of Faith and the Prophetic apart enough to where they are not able to draw on each other's power! I will only need a few more days and I will bring it all to pass!"

Satan really liked saying the words I WILL, for arrogance ran its course from beginning to end in him.

"There are only a few that can oppose us. Do we have their names?" Satan demanded.

"Yes sir," the demonic lieutenant replied, "one of the most dangerous is one named, Micah Cross."

"AGGHH!" Satan said with such fury that the chief lieutenant fell down trembling in fear. "Cross, his whole lineage was prophets! Through their ignorance I was able to manipulate most of them and steer them away from their calls. I even destroyed some of them, but this Micah Cross seems to have grabbed a hold of his call and has been a hindrance to me for a while now! Where is he now?"

"He's on an airplane sir, headed for the west."

"Hmm, dispatch the powers of the air in his direction to stop him." Satan ordered. "Kill him if possible."

"Yes sir," the lieutenant answered, and was gone.

Once out of sight of Satan, the demon lieutenant grimaced in pain as he rubbed the left side of his belly. No other evil spirit would have paid any attention to the open, constantly oozing, wound on the lieutenant's stomach. Neither would they have cared.

The Kingdom of Hell is always vying for position on how to overthrow each other. If the other dark spirits saw the lieutenant show any pain they would have recognized a weakness in him and would try to destroy him for his position. You see, nothing heals in the Kingdom of Hell and if a spirit had a gaping wound, and it did not seem to bother him at all, that spirit would be extremely feared by the others!

The lieutenant had a wound that was a massive gash and seemed to ooze all the time. Yet his deception was so complete that he managed to show no pain at all, as if it did not exist. This made him seem invincible to all the other dark spirits, and they were all afraid of him.

The lieutenant arrived in the air over Colorado. Hell had gained a stronghold there in 2008. Colorado is where the Altar of Incenses would burn if you overlaid the Tabernacle on the U.S. map! This was a strategic place to the devil. For this is where he had Barack Obama erect a duplicate of his throne in the Mile High Stadium on Invesco Field. Satan strategically did this; this is where it had to be placed.

In the skies just before you entered Colorado airspace, a conversation was taking place. The enemy's chief lieutenant had arrived on the scene and was briefing his forces there.

These spirits looked like small dragons. They had been responsible for downing planes for years. It was hard for them because the aviation world ran on such high laws; sometimes it took years to set up such neglect in the system that they could actually cause a downing.

"The master wants that plane down," the lieutenant said to the dragon spirits. "Do you understand?"

"Yes sir," they breathed out, "But sir, there is not enough neglect involved on these flights to down the craft" one of them said.

"Then attack it straight on and cause something," the lieutenant growled.

"Yes, sir, but that's impossible without a seed having been planted for it. The pilots on those aircrafts are not weak minded. They hardly even listen to the voices we try and plant in their thinking."

"I don't care what you have to do," the lieutenant said, "Satan wants that plane stopped!"

Just then the lieutenant opened his mouth as wide as a city bus as if he would devour the small dragons, the dragon spirits drew back in fear as the lieutenant roared out "JUST DO IT!"

His roar was with such a tremendous force that his hideous breath tried to form a tornado! With that, he was gone.

When the chief lieutenant roared, the plane Micah was on shook with turbulence.

These dragon spirits roamed the skies in small bands. They were like guerrilla forces, they attacked in groups of six to eight. This was a band of eight. They began to position themselves for the planes arrival into their airspace.

"There it comes," one said.

"I wonder who is on that plane," another asks, "that Satan wants it downed so badly. The way the lieutenant was acting you would think Micah Cross was on that plane." As the small dragon said that, they all looked at each other with great fear on their faces.

"You don't think that?" one dragon started to ask the leader.

"I don't know who or what, but look, it's almost here." The spirits positioned themselves for the attack.

Chapter 11

War in the Heavens

Their leader began to growl out orders: "you," he said pointing at one of the spirits, "you land on the top of the plane and try to damage the hull. You two," he barked, "it is too high for us to use any birds, so you two fly directly into the engines and try to make them malfunction! If nothing else, maybe we can create enough fear inside the plane to generate a seed large enough to bring it down! You three," he said, "get inside that cockpit and cause confusion any way you can! And you," he pointed to the last one, "you come with me and let's see if we can't get inside with the passengers. There's a chance that someone in there has sowed a seed for a heart attack or something. This way if we can't destroy the plane we can force them to land early. Now, GO!"

The eight spirits flew out to meet the plane.

One landed on the top and two crawled into the plane's engines. The spirit on the top began looking for a weak spot in the hull; the creature never saw the angel that landed behind him!

What the demons didn't know was that there was a force of angelic beings escorting that plane!

Just as the one dragons put out his claw to try and rip into the hull, an angel that worked with Micah stepped on his tail. Almost in the same instant the angel grabbed the spirit by the back of the neck, with his left hand; a grip that was absolutely unbreakable by the enemy spirit! As the dragon reached up to try and break the angels grip, he gasped in pain as the angelic soldier squeezed even tighter! The dragon's wings were flapping wildly, as he was gasping for his very existence.

While this was going on, another angel landed on the fuselage in front of the fight right above the plane's engines. The two dragons who were dispatched to fly into the engines and cause them to malfunction had crawled into the engines and had their tails still hanging out. The angel reached down with both hands took hold of each tail. The angel then began dragging them out! The dragon spirits knew the feel of that unbreakable grip and had a terrible dread upon them. They clawed and they clawed but they could not resist the force that was pulling them out! The angel dragged them and with a tail in each hand he began to swing them forward in a vertical circle one on each side! As he swung them over each shoulder he turned them loose at the exact same time, with a great force, hurling them toward the other angel who was standing on the tail of the other dragon!

While standing on the dragon's tail and gripping him with his left hand around the back of his neck, the angel took his right hand and drew a sword about six feet long and as the two dragons that were hurled toward him passed him on his right side, the warring angel sliced off both their heads in one swing in perfect timing as they passed by! The headless spirits bounced off the hull and fell off the side of the plane and disappeared as they fell to the earth!

Oh they would not cease to exist, but headless they were not nearly the threat they used to be. Wherever their heads landed they would lay and chew the dust, and make a barren spot on the ground. This is what the deserts are, grave yards for dragon spirits.

After slicing the heads off of the two dragons the angel threw the one he held by the neck straight up in the air with such a force the dragon could not use its wings. As it went up, a third angel appeared with a drawn sword. He made a horizontal slice and the dragons head was gone before it could even see what was coming! The angel watched as it fell toward the earth! The way those warring angels worked together was amazing! Their timing was perfect and without hesitation.

Inside the plane, the fight was about to begin. Unknown to the dragons inside the plane, the other three outside were gone! There were three people on the flight crew: the pilot, copilot, and one other sitting in the jump seat. The first dragon flew hard and fast toward the captain, but just before it collided with him, another war angel appeared seemingly out of nowhere and caught the spirit around the neck!

He was squeezing its neck with such a force, that the dragon, frantically, began to try and claw its way free but it was to no avail! The angel tightened his grip with such a force that it popped the head right off the dragon! The angel then threw the carcass towards the windshield. It passed right through the cockpit glass and disappeared falling below the nose of the plane. Its tail was the last thing that disappeared from view and the head followed the carcass on its own, already beginning its search for its body.

The other two demons in the cockpit were about to attack the other two members in the flight crew, but when the two dragons saw the angel, the attack broke off! The spirits went into full panic mode! One turned and bit the head off of the other and as its body fell to the floor of the plane, the angel drew his sword and ran it threw the remaining spirit, and then pinned it to the floor! The dragon spirit threw its head back and screamed in pain. With its eyes shut screaming, it never saw when the war angel drew another blade with his other hand

and cut its head off! Then the angel stuck the shorter blade into the head of the dragon like a skewer! He then picked up the body of the dragon impaled on the large blade and flung them both out of the front windshield!

Meanwhile, the body and head of the spirit whose head was bitten off had been lying very close together and had managed to join itself back together! It leaped toward the back of the angel but the angelic warrior tossed the blade that was in his left hand, flipping up in the air, and while it was suspended in the air, the angel, without looking, reached up over his left shoulder, before the evil spirit could even touch his back, and caught the dragon by the nose! The angel then threw him over his shoulder! But instead of letting the nose of the dragon go, he popped him like a whip and his head came loose from his body again and the evil spirits body kept going right out the windshield of the plane! The angel waited just a moment to create a space between the body and the head of the dragon then threw the head out as the blade he had tossed into the air landed gently, handle first, into his hand.

The last two spirits inside the plane with the passengers, not knowing what has befallen the others, were making their way down the aisle of the airplane. They were carefully looking at every magazine that was being read, they were listening to every conversation taking place.

One man was drinking a mixed drink and the small dragon spirit stuck its head right inside the body of the man, but to no avail, as he could only cause chest discomfort. Angrily pulling his head back out of the man it continued its search. A strange quietness, a sort of a lull had fallen over the people on the flight.

A Muslim man in the back of the plane suddenly spread a mat out in the floor and started his prayers. The dragon spirit never responded to it, as if he was not even there.

About that time a lady in a middle aisle seat repositioning herself in the seat just as the spirit passed by, frowned in discomfort and whispered "Jesus!" The Dragon, while not paying attention to the islamic prayers, suddenly jerked its head around to find who said that name! A fierce tremble of fear came across the evil spirit as he focused on the eyes of the lady who said it! Realizing it was not spoken in faith but just as a by-word, it turned back steadily making its way down the aisle.

While the one spirit continued in its search, the second spirit crawled upon the back of the flight attendant working each seat. It was clinging to her back with its head up beside hers! The flight attendant, not knowing this, tried to straighten up and had to put her hands on her lower back in pain. The spirit would leap back and forth from the back of one flight attendant to another! The evil spirit seemed to find relief as it landed on the backs of the attendants. At times, the spirit would land in the food of people as if it was trying to poison it.

The team Micah had assembled was a crack squad in the realm of the spirit. They knew how to press in with prophetic worship and God would open portals!

****

Intelligence Data on the Cross Team: THE TEAM

> Micah Cross: Male: Apostle, Prophet, Teacher, and Prophetic Musician

> Tommy Jensen: Male: Bass player, one who operated in dreams and visions.

> Socha : Female: Prophetic singer in worship and praise, singing in the Spirit

> Jordan: Female: Warrior, Preacher, plays any instrument, and powerful singer

> Rena: Female: One of the most powerful warriors on the team. Operates in prophetic dreams. A Pastor, who plays piano and Keyboard. Had done battle with numerous evil spirits and has defeated them!

* *

The team could sense something was wrong and went into war mode. Socha began to pray in the Spirit and Jordan started speaking the Word of God for the angelic host to do battle with!

The spirit that had been jumping from the backs of the flight attendants left the main floor and went down to the landing gear. It had found fear in one of the flight attendants who saw the landing gear on another flight malfunction and had become afraid the same thing would happen on this flight! This was what that spirit had been looking for! He took that seed of fear and had managed to cause it to start to malfunction! The sound was now being heard by the passengers, this was generating more and more fear and the landing gear was getting worse by the moment! The spirit was trying to create enough fear to cause a tragedy, or at least, make the airplane land prematurely!

Suddenly, Micah said: "I take authority over this plane! Every spirit of the damned that would try to bring this plane down, I bind you in Jesus name! You desist and stop in your maneuvers!"

The small spirit had managed to get the landing gear door to open a few inches. All at once the dragon's claws that it was using to dig into the landing gears functions became paralyzed! It could not use them!

Micah pressed in saying, "angels of the Lord go forth and

enforce these words and I will hold you accountable for the job you do in this situation!"

About that time the dragon that had been trying to cause a malfunction in the landing gear fell onto his back with his paralyzed claws! In pain with his eyes closed, it was distracted from everything around it. He never saw the war angel that walked up over him.

When the demon opened his eyes while laying there on his back, the spirit found himself looking up into the eyes of a warring angel with a drawn blade! The angel twirled his sword in a stabbing position, and was coming down at the dragon's chest. The evil spirit could not resist. Its scaly squeals of death blended in with the whirring of the landing gear motors as they started to work again! As the angel withdrew his sword, the creature slid through the crack it had managed to open in the gear door, the angel cut off its head just before it fell disappearing out of sight! The landing door closed and there were no more sounds.

There was only one more to deal with now. The leader of this band of spirits was still making his way down the middle of the aisle looking from left to right. Staring into the faces of each person, searching for a weakness large enough to exploit and make the pilot land that plane! Just as it swung its head back to the right, the spirit locked eyes with Micah Cross! The Holy Spirit had just then prompted Micah, and he had turned his head toward the aisle. Even though neither Micah nor anyone else could see the spirit physically, that dragon did not know if Micah could see him or not. The way Micah was staring at him, the spirit did not know if discerning of spirits was in operation or not!

It is a rude awakening to evil spirits when this happens and a human can actually see the spirit that is in operation.

The dragon locking eyes with Micah startled exclaimed, "Cross," with a hiss, "it's Micah Cross!"

With a look of total fear, that was the last words he said. At that very moment the hand of Micah's personal angel reached from behind Micah, and grabbed the dragon by the throat! The angels big hand wrapped all the way around the spirits neck! It looked as if the angel was almost connected to Micah, and his arm was an extension of Micah's arm. What the angel did next with the evil spirit was devastating! The angel dragged the spirit down the aisle by its neck. The foul spirit kept choking out the name Cross!

Once the angel got him to entrance door, it was so quick it was almost a blur. The powerful angel tossed the spirit up in front of him in the air and at the same time drew a massive blade, and while the spirit that was responsible for causing so many deaths was suspended in the air, the angel gripped his sword with two hands and swung the massive blade from above his head vertically splitting the spirit down the middle! Then before it could hit the floor the angel made a horizontal swipe and cut him in half!

With the word "Cross" on the dragons lips, the spirit that had wreaked havoc on so many lives, was laying in four pieces on the floor in front of the angel! An unseen force sucked the pieces through the door and it was gone!

After this, the plane seemed to calm down. Passengers were starting to talk again. You could hear laughter among the people again on the small jet. The very air seemed to have lightened. This whole spiritual battle had taken place on that plane and yet not one person other than Micah and his crew knew it.

Chapter 12

In Route

Upon Landing, the team started out on their two hour journey to the Ranch. There was joy among the team even though everyone knew this was very serious.

"Cross made it through sir," the chief lieutenant nervously reported to Satan.

"What!?" The head of filth exclaimed. "Can't any of these incompetent spirits accomplish anything?"

"Sir that was our elite squad, they've downed over a dozen planes that resulted in the death of hundreds! But there was a force on that plane unlike anything our operatives have ever encountered! We even had an Islamic on board who tried to summon the demons of Allah, but they were absolutely powerless against The Cross team," said the chief lieutenant.

"Then we must move faster than them. We only have a couple of hours to set something up before they arrive at the Ranch," Satan demanded.

"Yes," the demon answered.

"Have you tried to cause division within the team?" Satan asked.

"Yes sir," the demon answered, "but they seem to overcome each attack!"

"I'd like to kill that Cross!" Satan said. "Somehow I'm going to take him down. How much does Cross know of the plan?" Satan demanded.

"Sir, our sources suggest EVERYTHING!"

"WHAT?" the prince of darkness yelled. "How could this be?" "Oh wait, it's Him, the Spirit of Truth! I've been dealing with Him since Pentecost and He's caused my kingdom grief ever since. We have to up our game. Go ahead of The Cross team to that Ranch, with that many believers there for this meeting, there's bound to be religious spirits that some will bring with them. Tell them a direct order: stir it up! And to the spirits of envy and strife that are there, tell them also! In a body of people that big, there will be those susceptible to arrogance, pride, and jealousy. Stay on it! Get them to turn their swords on each other! You think those angels you face have blades; you do not want to face a believer's sword! Now, Go!"

With that, the demon was gone.

Micah and the team had stopped to rent music equipment they would need, since they were only able to fly a few key pieces with them. This added up to more time.

"It's close to being at full power Mother," the CERN scientist said. "By the 23rd, we will be there!"

"Yes!" Mother said excitedly. "This time we will be able to open the portal enough to bring them over! It was their technology that enables us to build all of this. They're not going to need much of an invitation.

Progress report?" Mother demanded. "Cooling?"

"Everything is running perfectly," the scientist replied.

"This time! This time!" Mother said excitedly, as she pulled out her private phone and began to call out a series of coded numbers. Then said, "Yes, everything is running perfectly. As long as Madonna does her job, there is enough sacrificed blood of children in the system, it will finally open!"

Hanging up the phone, the man on the other end of the line looked at the rest of the men in the room, he was a few years older, but he still possessed the same serpent features and still had the same evil heart! As he hung the phone up, he smiled and looked around at the other six in the room and said, "Well gentlemen it looks like you're going to get to see history made! The very RETURN OF APOLLO IS IMMINENT!"

Congratulations were then passed around the room to each other.

"Did you hear that?" Sä·na' said, as he flew up to the great lid and placed his ear on the underside of it. The other demons were mumbling to each other. "Silence fools!" Sä·na' shouted at the other spirits. "I need to hear!"

"Did you hear that?" Sä·na' growled again. "I've never heard the great lid make this sound!"

"It's not going to be long and it will open!" Sä·na' exclaimed! "Then at last, I'll be free to roam!"

"Let me hear!" a smaller foul spirit said as he flew up beside Sä·na' and placed his ear against the great lid.

Sä·na' suddenly enraged to a murderous attitude slapped the

smaller spirit and slammed it down onto the floor! Sä·na' didn't stop there, he flew down on top of the spirit and spread its arms out standing on each wrist the merciless Sä·na' took his massive claw and slowly pushed it into the creatures belly! The smaller spirit screamed and shrieked in pain! While the others started jumping and clapping in glee. Sä·na' smiled as he pulled his six inch talon from the smaller spirits belly. The creature rolled over whimpering like a small dog, and began trying to crawl away. Sä·na' kicked it and pointed at the others with his talon dripping with a dark ooze of decay that came from the creature's belly, "No one, I repeat, no one goes through that portal before me! Do you understand?"

The creatures looking at Sä·na' had hair like women, teeth like lions and tails like scorpions; they were waiting for the great lid to open.

The mindless hoards scurried away like rats in fear of Sä·na'. *I hate them all,* Sä·na' thought as he slid down against the wall in total darkness. In the distance the fallen angel heard the sloshing of the liquid, and the crunch of the teeth of those crocodiles as another damned soul was thrown into the pool.

As Sä·na' sat there in the darkness, so dark nothing could be seen, he contemplated devouring whatever he could in the earth when the great lid did finally open!

I'm not sure what's there now, Sä·na' thought. "But whatever spirit is next to Satan now is going to have to deal with me! I will rule again and woe to any of them who try to get in my way! Just like that spirit who challenged me before, no one takes my position as chief lieutenant, he was a fool!" Sä·na' said, as he held his right hand and began touch the end of each one of his enormous talons. The talon on his index finger was only half the size of the others. When Sä·na' felt of it he smiled a hideous wicked smile, "Where ever that spirit is, he will never forget the day I broke this off in his filthy belly! I can still hear him scream, whimpering as he crawled away! I just wish it had of been in front of the others. The fall happened so fast, no one knows I did that to him. Ha!" Sä·na' laughed "Wherever he's at now, I imagine he's had quite a time hiding that pain for all these centuries!"

Chapter 13

The Countdown Began

Everyone was excited to be at the ranch. Micah had been there once before about a year earlier. He had taught the Prophets the Absolute Goodness of God and everyone was looking forward to what he had to say. This time, Micah was there on a mission that no one knew about exactly.

Micah and his team had played prophetic worship for all of the other daytime meetings. It was now the last night of the two day gathering and everyone was excited with an anticipation of what the night held!

It was The 20th of September, 2015 and the countdown had begun. All of the Kingdom of Hell were beside themselves with excitement! The scientists at CERN were all abuzz. Everything was in place; the seven were watching the collider on close circuit television. Satan's tongue licked across his teeth as he anticipated devouring the human race!

At the ranch, Micah began speaking. He explained the throne of Satan, he told of CERN, the Pope, Madonna, and the portal that was set to open. Then the Holy Spirit said to Micah, "Have three Shofars blown." One in the back of the room, one in the middle of the room, and one from the stage! All three shofars were in a direct line from the stage to the back of the room. All of the shofar blowers were directed to blow towards Switzerland! It is not only the sound of the Shofar, but the children of God blowing the shofar is similar to when Jesus will descend from heaven with a shout, with the voice of the archangel, and with the sound of a trumpet or Shofar!

There was one Shofar sounded in the back of the room by a powerful prophet from the west. In the middle of the room was the host of the meeting, a powerful visionary, he sounded his shofar, and on the stage, Socha, part of Micah's team, sounded a shofar.

They were instructed to sound them three times toward Switzerland! Then Micah and the crowd of powerful prophets shouted and told those fallen beings in Jesus name, to stay in that other dimension! That they could not cross into this realm! It was powerful how that prophetic crowd ripped into those spirits with authority! The very air seemed to be charged with overwhelming power! At the end of the night you could see visible smoke in the room! It looked like a war zone after a battle. There was smoke that resembled the kind that appears after fireworks explode hovering over the field.

A Seer, came and told Micah in her words, that she saw a rat run into CERN and shut it down!

All at once in Switzerland, the collider began to lose power! Just enough that the portal could not open! A burning smell began to fill the room.

"Wait something is wrong!" Mother declared.

Scientists began to scramble in the underground facility. Unseen power began to fill the atmosphere around them disrupting their flow of power! Hideous faces that were set to finally make it into this realm were poised to come through the portal! The scientists were just starting to see them when it began to fade! On the other side of the great lid, little did the scientists know that the faces they were seeing was Sä·na' in the lead with hordes of creatures standing behind him ready to come through when the first crack of the great lid opened.

"Get ready," Sä·na' growled out to the hoards behind him! "When that lid cracks open enough to get through, we must move!"

The sound coming from the lid seemed to be getting close to reaching a peak, and the great lid began to shake like never before! Then Sä·na' noticed a slight decrease in the sound!

"NO! NO!" Sä·na' screamed as he began to slam himself against the great lid! "Push you fools, push!" He yelled out!

They all began to push hard against the lid, pinning Sä·na' between them and the great lid until decay oozed out of Sä·na''s ears.

The power level at CERN began to die down more and more!

Sä·na' reached his talons up and placed them against the underside of the lid as he saw his chance to go through it fading away! It had come so close to opening and the veil between the natural and the spirt world had come so close that he could even vaguely see a face from the other side! What Sä·na' did not know was that it was Mother he was looking at. He saw as she stretched her hand toward Sä·na''s talons as his image slowly faded away.

Mother sat down sobbing.

On the other side of the lid Sä·na' fell exhausted to floor of the great cave weak from his effort to push the lid open! Sä·na' almost deaf with the sound of the echoing Shofars in Idaho he groggily looked up as the hordes of dark spirits that had pressed him between against the lid, noticed the ooze leaking from his ears. The leader of them reached down with its finger and touched the decaying ooze, putting it to his mouth. When the spirit tasted it, he went wild screaming! Then all the other spirits began screaming with him! Then, just as if they were ordered to, they all together attacked Sä·na' to devour him! It looked like a feeding frenzy! The smell of the ooze leaking from Sä·na''s ears seemed to pull them all down on him! Sä·na' disappeared under the pile of spirits that engulfed him! He, too weak to resist, reached his hands with his great talons toward the lid, but it wasn't long before his hand grew limp and disappeared under the great pile of devouring spirits.

The team left for the airport the next day. The flight home was peaceful enough, the team sat quiet having been through such a time. The rest of the people on the plane to Micah's knowledge, never knew that anything had happened.

Chapter 14

Epilogue

Micah knew this was not going to be the last battle he and his team would be engaged in, but through the Word of God and the power of The Mighty Holy Ghost, they would be ready!

It had been over 7 months since the prophetic meeting in Idaho, Micah had just finished his devotion one morning and as he turned on his computer the headlines told that a WEASEL had knocked the Large Hadron Collider offline! Micah smiled as he thought about it, I mean after all, what does a weasel look like but an overgrown rat?

Oh chapter 14?

UNTIL NEXT TIME

ROBIN D. BULLOCK

Contact
Information

To order more copies of this book, or other titles by
Robin D. Bullock

Contact

Robin D. Bullock
P. O. Box 67
Warrior, AL 35180

www.robindbullock.com
robindbullockoutreach@gmail.com

Other Titles by Robin D. Bullock

God Is Absolutely Good

Jesus, Why It Is The Way It Is!